−.50

BODY SECRETS.........

If you let it, the body will tell you its secrets.

And having told them, will be free to move on.

This is a book about listening to those secrets.

BODY SECRETS..........

Unwinding Your Historical Limitations

Don McFarland

A handbook for bodyworkers, healers,
........and other apprentice sorcerers.

Shi'Zen Publications

Published by Healing Arts Press 1988
First published in UK by Shi'Zen Publications 2006
PO Box 57, Hebden Bridge
West Yorkshire, HX7 6WW
United Kingdom
www.shizen.co.uk

Printed in Great Britain by the Charlesworth Group, Huddersfield

McFarland, Don
Body Secrets, Unwinding Your Historical Limitations

Library of Congress Catalogue Card Number 88-080896
ISBN 0 9539 0743 0

Fourth printing

I dedicate this overture to:

Ida Rolf who had the vision and cleared the way. On occasion I find her picture smiling on me. I relish those smiles.

Sondra Ray who teaches me by example...and reminds me that there are truly no limitations but my own.

Hans Viking Axelson who teaches the world a more healthy way of life and whose visionary quest makes me feel good.

Judith Aston who blends an understanding of body mechanics with a flair for design that suggests a more comfortable world ahead for us all.

All my wonderful clients and colleagues and friends and students who have directed my work over the years. You are really quite spectacular teachers. Thank You!

With unbounded appreciation......

I thank God that I am allowed to do this work.

I thank all the Saints and Masters who have made their presence known to me in so many ways.

I am grateful for the blessings and guidance of Jesus.

I am grateful for the presence of Babaji.

I am grateful to all the devas and all the guides in all their shapes and forms from whatever realm they come. I am always ecstatic when they pop in for a visit now and again and sometimes linger to oversee our work.

I thank those special guides who are always with me when I need them most. I thank the council I so vividly encountered in Peru.

I thank all the Breathers who make our world a more exciting playground.

I thank you Linda for enriching my life beyond all my expectations.

I thank the Universe for its incredible gift of unlimited abundance.

CONTENTS

A tribute to Don and his work.

I would honestly say that in my opinion Don McFarland is an expert and authority on the subject of bodywork. What qualifies me to say that? Well in the last decade I have had approximately 150 Rolfing sessions plus hundreds of other kinds of bodywork sessions also. I had these all over the world with all types of bodyworkers so I do have a lot to compare to. It was because of all this bodywork I was able to stay on the road constantly without falling apart. I was quite literally "always on tour."

All the people who worked on my body everywhere helped me and I acknowledge them; but it was not until I met Don that I found it all come together. A magic happened. My body seemed to respond and move and change when he just looked at me. He would literally speak to my tissue and it responded. By the time he touched me it was already moving in the right direction somehow and he went with it. There was never any pain and yet there was more change than usual.

How could this happen? Obviously because of the fact that all the multitudes of courses he had taken and all the experience he had had somehow was harmonized in *him*. In his presence my body went into harmony. But maybe even more significant was that he let my body speak to him. He seemed to be in psychic communion with my body and he would take it where it knew it should go. I could be totally "out of it," exhausted, burned out, unable to communicate well and yet he and my body would "talk" in a very intelligent manner and I would go away from the session being totally rejuvenated.

I would also like to acknowledge Don as an extremely committed human being to the service and healing of mankind. Many times he has travelled long distance when I needed help without batting an eye. Even in India, high up in the Himalayas, he worked on my students, constantly above and beyond the call of duty without pay.

We all have a lot to learn from experts. If you are already a bodyworker and want to learn more you will definitely appreciate this book. It will save you years of study. If you are thinking about becoming a bodyworker I know you will be inspired by Don. If you are just reading this to learn more about your body, you are wise.

I know Body Harmony is the perfect name for Don's work. Approximately the same day Don came up with this title I had a dream in which a band was playing a tune "Perfect Harmony." I acknowledge you Don McFarland for helping me to achieve more and more perfect harmony.

How to Use This Book....

This is a book for you who would understand and renegotiate the secret agreements made by your egos in the name of survival. It's a remembrance of the easy and graceful physicality that has always been your birthright but which you may have temporarily misplaced.

It's a handbook for you who practice the art of bodywork in any of its forms...to extend your influence into new arenas. It's also a book for you who are receiving, are about to receive, or are even considering receiving bodywork...to focus your goals and enhance your processing.

But most of all this book is a reminder and an invitation. A reminder that whenever you place a hand upon another, no matter what the occasion or intent, at that moment, for better or worse you have become a bodyworker. Like it or not, your most casual touch does influence both the shape and the function of the body before you, just as your own body is influenced in return.

Since you already speak the language, consider this your invitation to listen once again to the old time subtleties and awaken once more to the healing powers of your touch.

Since all healing starts with looking beyond those illusions that obscure the nature of reality, throughout this book, as throughout life, please look beyond the ubiquitous illusion of duality and consider the roles of bodyworker and client as completely interchangeable. Consider how appropriate it is to assume both roles at the same time. Actually it's not only appropriate...it's unavoidable!

And if the concepts or the words sound unfamiliar, if it seems strange to conceive of listening as well as looking with your hands, and your heart, then reorganize your perceptual framework and allow yourself the luxury of understanding touch as the multisensory experience that it is. Then you may come to smell as well as taste the feel of good bodywork. It's all circulating somewhere out there in the ethers you know.

You may wish to consider the first few chapters as a conceptual framework for the mechanics that follow. Or you may not. It's impossible to factor out the elements of productivity. The magic comes as much from the climate as it does from the mechanics.

Remember, everything that follows is based on clinical observation, on bodywork experience rather than on any particular philosophy. This is a practical book concerned with practical matters. This is a book of practical magic. Sun Bear, a very practical native American medicine man, has said that if your philosophy doesn't grow corn he doesn't want to hear about it. Listen well then, for this is a book about growing corn.

If I Tell You My Secrets...

...Will You Respect Me in the Morning?

Who knows what secrets lurk in the hearts of men?

The Shadow knows...but you know how shadows are.

The Ego knows............but it won't tell.

And the Body knows...............but the body talks in riddles.

Well, it doesn't really talk in riddles you know. It only seems that way. It's just that the body prefers to keep its own counsel, as well it might after taking such a back seat to the intellect for so long. Apparently it has become reconciled to not being taken seriously anyway, after all it's **only** a body!

So there it sits atop all that primordial wisdom, content to quietly tantalize us with occasional bursts of insight that we only half believe in any case. No wonder it prefers to embrace us in elusive shadows that remain always a whisper beyond our comprehension.

Only a body indeed!

It's only logical then that its most important message to us remains its most obscure: that wonderful message of assurance that at the very core of its being, this body of ours is only a reflection of all the other aspects of the self; a structural heritage that derives its shifting parameters from the mental, and the emotional, as well as the spiritual aspects of the soul.

It's a reflection...and an extremely accurate reflection at that...but who listens?

As the body so persistently reminds us there is another dimension to this great secret, for this mirroring works its magical effects in both directions. Hesitantly, shyly, and yet tenaciously the body demonstrates that when the **complete** self works as a **unified** field, rather than in isolated fragments, our potential approaches the unbounded and our reach extends well beyond the limits of whatever at the time we deem to be The Possible.

Whatever lies beyond these limits we have set upon ourselves is only what we have bargained away during negotiating sessions with an overcautious ego.

Personal and private limitations may originate in any aspect of the self, but **once accepted they become anchored within the tissues of the body itself. Physically anchored!**

The body stands as a living affirmation of the mechanical realities behind this largely ignored process. We seldom notice the all-important, life-shaping negotiations that take place between the ego and the body in the wee small hours where the ego feels secure enough to hammer out a pact and classify it as secret. Which it then files carefully away within the security of a semi-compliant tissue structure.

The ego prefers that from this point on the whole business never again be mentioned. Just not in good taste you know!

However, the body is also covertly clear about this being a two way street. **What has become anchored can also become unanchored**...and the technology for the process has been programmed into the tissues from the very beginning...and even now resides quietly and obscurely amid the unexplored landscapes that comprise the suburbs of physicality.

To access all this inherent potential is only a matter of remembering the language and of listening to what the tissues are willing to tell us and then of following instructions exactly as given. Which requires that we actively infiltrate into the ominous realm of the secrets themselves.

Notes on the character of secrets.....

Before we enter their backyard, there are certain things we must understand about the nature of secrets and about the pacts they have made with the ego.

When dealing with secrets be forewarned that they are possessed of quite beguiling traits. They are incredibly soothing and charming, but they are equally renowned as sirens and masters of seduction as well.

Secrets support all the little fantasies of the ego...and collaborate with it to meet the expectations of the world, as perceived through ego-colored glasses of course.

Body Secrets

For its part the ego creates a home within for its co-conspirators, and this is precisely the intersection where our limitations are anchored and our dreams held prisoner. This is precisely the crossroads where as healers we enter straight away into The Reluctant Zone.

It is secrets we are engaging here, and secrets have their own priorities, survival being the foremost. It is built into the nature of a secret to keep a low profile, for it stands to lose more than its identity if exposed. Its very existence is at stake. The security of a secret lies in anonymity. A secret that is very good at its trade can exist almost indefinitely unsuspected by even its closest neighbors. Almost but not quite.

While secrets promise survival for all of the ego's private mythologies, there is a price to be paid. Secrets do not reside loosely nor easily within the confines of a body. They hold the tissues in an unrelenting grip of strangulation. Secrets flourish in an atmosphere of physical compression and rigidity.

The ego sleeps more securely, but the price to the body...and therefore to the soul...is always some loss of physical freedom, as well as a corresponding loss in all those countless freedoms that transcend the physical as we now understand the physical. The more awesome the secret, the greater the degree of loss.

Secrets are unsuspected saboteurs that progressively burden the body with concerns that it never quite manages to carry with any real sense of style.

Secrets are so insidiously powerful that all who would offer them hospitality eventually become their prisoner.

It's more than just our structure that pays the price of a compromised ego. To some extent each of our actions, voluntary and involuntary, become increasingly compromised as well.

We evolve into reservoirs of physical microrigidities that tend to obscure the trails and cover the existence of our secrets. We evolve into a collection of minor and not-so-minor rigidities that in their totality are physically responsible for shaping the limits of **all** of our ongoing behaviors.

It takes effort, vigilant effort...a.k.a. stress...to keep these secrets under the covers and out of sight.

Out of sight, out of mind, says the ego with fingers crossed.

Not quite! ...whispers a body that dreams covert dreams of a forbidden freedom. Quietly defiant, the body envisions an eventual unburdening. But even though this is precisely of what the body dreams, it is also precisely what the ego fears the most. If anything, the ego has an active imagination and is well aware of the gruesome possibilities that might repose in those areas occupied by its secret allies. It dreads this obscure landscape of the great unknown that is surely populated with what must be literally uncountable **monsters of the What If.**

What Ifs of so many varieties and sizes and shapes and colors that even the most intrepid ego must be excused for its show of timidity while standing at the brink.

What if these secrets that hide behind the mask were never meant to be seen in the light of day? Might we unwittingly unleash some primordial shade from its nether-world imprisonment? And what might this portend? How can a poor ego ever be sure just what effects such actions might have upon an already all too shaky universe?

This internal dialogue of mindless gossip is **only ego talk!** ...these are just the sounds of an ego-created fear that exists only within the confines of an ego-created reality. But it exists nevertheless and therefore it must be dealt with accordingly.

The body itself always opts for freedom. It despises all forms of physical tyranny and banks its hopes on the sure knowledge that secrets have one absolutely mortal enemy, one old nemesis that travels the road under the name of *Rhythm.*

Even the most entrenched secrets have never been able to hold their own for any length of time once they find themselves facing graceful and fluid movements undulating throughout their landscapes. Between these two there can be no compromise. Rhythm either goes around a secret and scares it half to death, or directly through the secret washing it away upon a pulsating tide that leaves nothing behind it but a vague and emotionless memory.

When we introduce rhythm into the body we are entering directly into the unexplored territory of What If. This is the juncture where the body also appreciates a friend, it too becomes timid at times, it too needs reassurance along the way.

Body Secrets

As healers we can become that friend and supply that reassurance if we would only conduct our business in an atmosphere of understanding and safety. **Complete understanding and absolute safety**...in the presence of which it becomes relatively effortless to coax the secrets out into the light, and thereby considerably ease this cleansing of the tissues.

An important aspect of this process called body is its continuous, if largely ignored, attempts at communicating with us. If we would truly understand this process in its entirety, it is not enough that we attend only to the obvious, to the shouts, we must listen to the wee small whispers as well.

Particularly to the smallest and the quietest of the whispers. It is by way of these gentle and unobtrusive communications that the most guarded of secrets are offered up for the sharing. And it is precisely through this sharing that the freeing of the body begins.

On occasion the body will appear hesitant and suspicious, but that's only on the surface. Somewhere, sometime in the past this body has most assuredly been trifled with to some extent or another. But despite the scars of historical mistreatment something from deep within understands our interests and our intentions and if our interests and intentions coincide with its own, Jackpot! The body begins to quiver with anticipation, relishing this prospect of finally unwinding itself from its most secret of secrets.

The body has its dreams. Each and every body harbours the dream of casting off its burdens and running naked on the beach, it dreams the dream of a kindred soul out there able to understand its language in all its richness, one able to speak all the dialects, and relishes most of all its vision of an enlightened playmate to share the yellow brick road with.

The body understands all about this yellow brick road, even if the ego doesn't dare.

The yellow brick road...a.k.a....**the bodywork trail.** Which is the way to escape the asphyxiating confines of your historical limitations.

This is your way out. And there really is such a road out there you know. It's unfamiliar at times only because its exact nature tends to be obscured by an overcautious ego.

Upon first encountering this road, few recognize it for what it is. I certainly didn't, but even at that early stage some part of my spirit danced with an instinctive knowing that I had stumbled upon wonderous possibilities for exquisite adventures into the unknown and unknowing aspects of the soul.

I've explored its trails and wandered its byways for quite a while now and I still haven't begun to discover where it ultimately might be leading. No one really knows all that's to be found at the other end...at any of the countless other ends...if there is such a thing as an end. It's difficult enough to imagine beforehand all the exquisite and wonderous images one is likely to encounter along the way. On this trip the rewards of the journey itself more than offset any tribute the ego chooses to demand of us.

Body Secrets

It's a stroll among cloudy remembrances of things long past, through landscapes of delicately personal memorabilia that combine and twist into sultry dream-time delights that wrap themselves in the arms of historical shadows which immediately melt into unimagined yet clearly distinct promises. Promises obscured only by the illusions the ego still deems necessary to some archaic survival plan.

There are exquisite markers all along this pathway, the legacies of all who went before to smooth the way...ghostly footprints of Ida Rolf standing suspiciously close to a memory of Merlin...mementos from Daniel David Palmer, the founder of Chiropractic just slightly to the left of Andrew Still, the founder of Osteopathy...both heavily marked over with graffiti from Moshe Feldenkrais and Wilhelm Reich...all decorated with the countless smiles and tears bequeathed to us by the ancient and the modern men and women of physical medicine, and psychic medicine, and energy medicine, which are all found to be exactly the same thing...markers from all the shamans and the healers and the wizards and the enchanters and the alchemists blending smoothly with the present day wizardry of such as Marion Rosen and John Upledger and Judith Aston and Hans Axelson and the many others who carve out timeless parables to be savored by us all...

It's a wonderous road this...but make no mistake about one thing...**this is a toll road**...and an expensive one at that!

If I Tell You My Secrets...

Or so it seems at times. Actually what at first appears extravagant, will prove on detailed calculation to be one of life's great bargains.

What the road eventually demands from each of us is all those familiar and comforting illusions of the ego. The longer one walks the road the more of them it demands.

The cost? Personally it has cost me almost everything that I once had, or rather that I thought I had, which on closer inspection turned out to be not so very much at all.

Expense is just another of the self-delusions we use to keep ourselves stuck. In point of fact the returns always exceed the investment. Dividends from my own meager ante have been more than I once dared imagine possible.

Dividends such as a life that works and the blessings of an international community of enlightened friends and companions and the occasional company of angels...plus the ecstasy of a look into the face of infinity...an experience, a knowledge and a recognition of the Divine.

In case you haven't been here before.........**Welcome** to this magical highway and yes it is deceptive and yes it will continue to be deceptive. At times it will appear as an expressway, while at others it will seem little more than a suggestion.

Nevertheless, consider this your invitation to walk a ways and, if you dare, to reconnect with some forgotten wonders you may have dropped off just the other side of a misplaced dream. You will find that on this journey a body that functions ever more gloriously is the barest beginnings of the trip.

On this pathway it is more than likely that you will stumble once again upon those obscure gates which open your deepest recesses and call forth your dimly remembered excitements that prove exhilarating and frightening all in the same breath and where you may encounter your soul adrift on a voyage of inward adventure...a voyage that recalls the countless faces of sensuality...which may be uncomfortable to the ego but which holds up a mirror to the soul that twinges on the almost unbearably beautiful.

For this is that fabled pathway of esoteric secrets, of questions yet to be asked face-to-face and heart-to-heart and of answers that only the enlightened and the brave dare to acknowledge out loud.

Make no mistake, however, stepping onto this roadway is the crossing of your own private Rubicon. It is here you sign the pact and unlock the gate, here you begin the releasing of the very secrets you hold most dear. And know this with certainty: having once released these secrets, you can never again return to the comforts of unconsciousness from whence you came.

Do not mistake this for dramatics. **It's merely a statement of the way these things work.**

This is a road of quiet combat. Entering here is the beginning of a campaign to liberate your soul as well as your body.

Traditional military wisdom dictates that you begin any such campaign fortified with the necessary support troops, all moving together under a tested strategy. As it is with any campaign, look first to your terrain, consider your objectives, then select whatever tactics seem most likely to insure you success. Such considerations may be viewed as **the etiquette of the road.**

As it is with any form of sorcery your very first consideration must be your frame of reference, that point of view that will so strongly influence all of your interactions from here on in.

Whatever attitude that you go in with now will largely determine what you come out with later. It may even be the single most important variable in the equation.

Let a well-chosen attitude then serve as your point of embarkation and do not gloss this over lightly for it is not a statement of philosophy. It is nothing more than the simple recognition of what factors work the most efficiently in a given situation, no more than an acknowledgment of the magic capable of being generated through the application of an attitude that is exquisitely appropriate to a precise situation.

All that follows is exactly what I have observed to work the most consistently and the most effectively. The emphasis throughout is on efficiency and economy of effort, which in the accounting may prove to be exactly the same thing. Satisfactory results are fathered by efficient behaviors. The more efficient the behavior the more noble the offspring.

Body Secrets

Any event of stature owes its initial impetus and its final shape to the parenting provided by the functional encouragement of an appropriate and friendly attitudinal framework.

The magic starts with an attitude, which is really nothing more than a posture, an orientation of the body in connection with an action...or a mood...or a way of acting...or of feeling...or of thinking. It may equally well be a disposition, or a mental set, or leaving the Earth for a moment, the position of a spacecraft of whatever kind, in relation to a given line or plane.

Posture and attitude it appears then are intrinsically linked together, attitude inseparably bound to a posture. And it is worth noting that both the structural and the functional postures that emerge through any bodywork transaction can be accurately predicted beforehand by looking into the attitudes and, if you will, the postures of the two participants.

This interaction of bodyworker and client begins to assume its own life and its own shape with a meeting of respective attitudes, which are accurately reflected in the respective postures, and how well these mesh with each other will give direction and form to all their subsequent endeavors together.

It is of prime importance that we recognise how basic this is to our work. Efficiency demands that we proceed from whatever position that is most likely to maximize our chances of meeting therapeutic goals, whatever those goals and whatever that position might be.

And what produces the most effective results is an uncompromising attitude of absolute respect for the body before you.

This is the foundation for our work, it's so very basic, and so very important that it can not be overstated. What is needed on the part of both participants is....

* Respect for this body before you, because that is what works most efficiently.

* Respect for this body before you as it is right now at this very moment...not how it was...or will be...or should be...or might be with a few modifications...but **exactly as it is right now!**

Bathed in this warmth of appreciation, the body glows and becomes inclined to relax its defenses a bit and entertain the possibilities of expanding its parameters.

Where no defense is perceived as necessary growth naturally occurs, and the body naturally begins to reclaim its innate freedoms...possibly its birthright of consummate grace and flexibility which you know was only misplaced somewhere along the road anyway.

And within this climate of respect the body is also able to more smoothly and easily assimilate its new prerogatives into a fully functioning unit...and all is well.

However......

Body Secrets

There may be a problem on your horizon. Many of the bodies you will see are exceptionally easy to respect.

It's difficult not to value the dancer, or the athlete, or any of those who move with grace. A grace that's a physical acknowledgment of the divine. A grace so obviously lacking in the rigid and defended posture. It's easy to respect all those who truly respect themselves, that's the easy part of the situation, but....

There are other bodies out there. Bodies with different and somewhat disturbing messages. What do we do about those bodies?

How do we address ourselves to the shameless, shapeless lumps that masquerade as bodies, and lurch into our offices displaying no sense at all of how a decent body should be about its business?

How are we to react to these walking encyclopaedias of abuse and neglect that are a living slap in the face to whatever sense of aesthetics we lay claim to, what do we do about these so-called bodies?

Well maybe we better just recognize that we are only looking into one of the many faces of dissonance, which after all is only a defensive posturing of the ego.

We might just as easily be confronted with the disharmony of a vocally pleasant and likable client who has somehow attached his charming self to a body that habitually screams indiscriminate challenges to the world.

Whatever, it's still just another face of dissonance, and as it is with all such conflicting messages that walk through your doorway it's only the ego making its poorly concealed declaration of fear.

The ego makes its statement....and the body winks. **Listen to the body!**

Whatever the challenge confronting us, we must be clear that our attitude is too important to the process to be only a reflexive response to a provocative presentation.

Of course there are choices to be made in the selecting of clientele. You may decline to work with such as these and that is clearly a legitimate decision. Techniques for choosing your clients as well as your bodyworker will be discussed later, but for now understand that if you should elect to work with this client, then ethically you owe it to the both of you to enter this contract under the most effective conditions possible. It is therefore imperative that you respect the body that stands before you or else you cheat yourself at least as much as your client and the quality of all your future interactions together will suffer for it.

Overcoming any such negative considerations you have about a particular body is really not that difficult. It starts with the taking of a deep breath, and allowing the ease that accompanies a full, natural exhalation to lift the veil of recognition...and then to acknowledge that common thread that weaves its way through all the bodies that enter your offices...that factor common to them all that merits your authentic respect.

It is quite simple to honor this body once you recognize it for what it is. A survivor of obscure but vitally important wars. A decorated veteran.

Body Secrets

No matter what shape it's in now, this body before you has physically endured to this point in time. It is more than just alive. It is not on hold. It has somehow managed to maneuver itself into your offices and, if for nothing else, this warrants your esteem. For all those who make it this far carry the indelible **mark of the winner!**

There have been so many others who just could not handle life at all. So many found lacking in that vital force, or courage, or desire, or whatever it is that is necessary to propel one into your offices.......but this body is not one of those. This body stands before you present and accounted for, which is an accomplishment of not insignificant proportions!

No matter how convoluted this structure remember that it does represent a successful adjustment to life. You are looking at a singular system of adaptation that has become crystallized into the flesh; at a method of defense this ego/body complex has chosen to fight its fights; at physical patterns that may be directly responsible for the very survival of this somewhat intact individual, whose body may not look like it celebrates in present time, but at least retains a blueprint and a memory and a potential for future celebrations.

You are looking at the outward manifestations of inward tissue strategies, the physical form of ego survival mechanisms that have performed services valuable enough to have once been counted as indispensable. With the blessings of the ego, each has remained behind to run roughshod over the very same landscapes it originally contracted to protect.

If I Tell You My Secrets...

Only now it's a more secret landscape to be sure, for in a quite substantial sense, what you see here has the deceptive elements of a smokescreen that obscures the basic issues and diverts your eyes from the scent of some particularly clandestine hideaway.

Such tissue adaptations do have a certain flair about them. A quality that eventually becomes as familiar to the body as it is to the ego and the paradox here is that such familiarity creates a strange side effect, an atmosphere of ego comfort that exists within an ambience of basic distress. No matter how much the discomfort, at least there are no What Ifs here, no surprises. This is a thoroughly known entity.

Look then to these veteran warriors with eyes of respect for the services they have rendered.

The problem now is that these comrades of yesterday have become an embarrassment to the body of today.

However, the ego does not wish to reconsider the situation at all, to the ego this recalls remnants of carefully disremembered fears, which it prefers to keep disremembered.

But the body knows it has outgrown the association. It recognizes spectres from an earlier time and acknowledges that conditions have changed, that the situation is out of step with the requirements of today. This the body freely acknowledges.

The body chooses the present.
The ego prefers the past.

The body understands just how much these relics impede its progress.

The ego understands that they are known trouble-shooters, and that one can count on them in times of trouble.

The ego has this phobia about the unknown. It dreads the What Ifs it knows must surely lie in wait for it throughout the future tense. What if....Heaven forbid!...we should ever require these services again?

This is **the basic dilemma of bodywork.** Whether to stay with the security of the known...or to risk what little comfort there is available in familiarity...and go gallivanting throughout the precarious landscapes of a fathomless and holy instant in pursuit of a quite elusive promise.

Ostensibly the client comes seeking your help, seeking freedom from the hold of obsolete habit patterns. But should his fears now exert themselves, remember that up to now these secret knights of the ego have held an exclusive contract and this could be the edge. Don't push! Don't rush! This could be the point where he first encounters the unobscured face of fear, and he may choose to back off.

The only ethical procedure is to then downgrade your primary goal to one of **loosening** the grip of exclusivity that binds him to his limitations....and soothe him with the assurance that at some later time, at the coordinates of his choice, he will once again be free to throw down the gauntlet and go the route...as he chooses.

If I Tell You My Secrets...

As healers we then have the distinct honor of helping our client dismantle the franchise.....helping him extend his options...helping him ease out his old restrictions, with all due acknowledgment and respect of course, making sure that he understands that he does not have to dismiss them forever, that he can always call them back should he feel the need...but call them back at his discretion.

This is a new day with new rules. Never again will they come as absolute masters who run the show and dictate the terms as they will.

From this moment on they come as allies to perform a momentary service and then to graciously and quietly take their leave once more.

From this point on the body lives in present time...and assumes supreme sovereignty over its own fate and fortunes.

...and the answer to our original question turns out to be one of the following:

(1) a resounding yes
(2) of course
(3) no worries mate
(4) all of the above

The question only came from the dark recesses of the ego in the first place. With our secrets having been fully told we are free and with the morning light there comes an even greater, an even more enduring Respect.

Configurations of the Soul.....

.....Body as Playground

The soul finds its physical representation in the structure of the body, and the body we exhibit today is completely of our own making. It's our history solidified in living flesh, a testimony to our dramas, and what may be even more ominous, a library of all our past adventures and misadventures on public display for all the world to witness. The structural as well as the functional aspects of this fantastic unit both store and illustrate all the details of our incomplete memories.

Incomplete, unfinished, and stuck. Physically stuck, physically compressed into the tissues. The ego caches the more sensitive issues so deeply and so cleverly that they remain secreted even from our conscious selves. Particularly and especially from our conscious selves.

The ego manages to conveniently forget about these events, but the body never does. Within each pulsating mass of tissue there reside absolutely incredible tales, just waiting for an audience, just waiting for the possibility to be heard and to be considered on their merits.

They constitute the most improbable adventures imaginable, and they are all available to us for the listening. For the body knows that having once been completely and truthfully told, it will be free of them forever.

The tissues making up our body configurations are only one of the ways in which we present ourselves to the world, but they are certainly our most accurate statement. Truth may be lacking in a person's words but it is always present in their tissues. To witness it is only a matter of listening for the call of the whisper and then coaxing it out into the open. The tissues never lie to us. They don't know how.

So look at the shape of success. Look then to this body before you with eyes of appreciation for that success. And when you touch this body, touch it with the very same appreciation. Recognize the beauty within, and then let your touch honor and enhance that beauty.

Beauty is always to be found when you take the time to look for it. Seek it out and use it as your foundation to build a better body.

This is the framework of successful transformation, a proven framework that works infinitely better than ferreting out the ugly and then trying to exorcize it.

The key point here is respect. **Respect for what is, in order to create what can be.** Respect facilitates change. When in doubt just remind yourself that this body is an accumulation of patterns that have smoothed out a rough road, and that without their presence the road may have become just a little too rough at some juncture.

But this is not the time for sentimentality, it's time now to cut loose obsolete obstructions so that the soul can be on about its business. The soul and the body, and each bearing such a reciprocal impact on the other. The soul always travels lighter and quicker without excess bodily luggage.

With this in mind, this is where we sincerely thank these veterans for services rendered, and discreetly present them their discharge papers. This is where we create a ceremony of retirement, which is simplicity itself: we physically assist the tissues in unlocking their vaults and airing out their musty secrets. Through the auspices of our hands, our souls whisper a rhythmic reminder into the tissues, a reminder that preaches Potential.

The mechanics of our methodology insist that we look first within ourselves. Our effectiveness depends upon the degree to which we clearly understand the state of our own current limitation system. Present-time personal limitations are limitations on our work. To achieve maximum effectiveness, to not limit our client's possibilities, we must reduce our own areas of unconsciousness.

Which is not so formidable a task as it might sound. It begins with awareness, which is nothing more than focusing a light on our own secret areas. Then our work itself will expand our awareness...exactly as our newly expanded awareness will in turn expand the quality of our work. The client becomes our metaphor, as we help him release his area of interest we address exactly that same area within ourselves.

Consider the Textures of Limitation.

The biggest stumbling block may once again be **Attitude** which continues to cast an ever present shadow over all these transactions...

...and since this is above all else a practical book......

    ....in order to tune up your instrument
    ....in the spirit of self discovery
    ....as part of your bodywork process

...consider now if you will, the fundamental question of how you personally feel about the possibility of change itself.

How you really feel about it. Listen within, feel exactly how your body responds to such matters.

Bodies change of course. Time takes its toll and eventually wears us down. We can see that. That's the self-evident observation.

But what about the other side of the coin, the other less frequent observation? Is this process of change a two way street?

Wait... and listen for an answer to each of your questions. **Listen**... to your body, listen to your rhythms, listen to your breathing and your heart rate. Listen and feel. **Feel**... the tightness, and the looseness, and the dissonance from within.

Is it just as possible to change for the better as it is for the worse?

Is it possible for a body to actually rejuvenate itself, or only to slowly crumble away?

Is it possible for any body to rejuvenate itself?

Is it even possible for your particular body to rejuvenate itself?

Consider this process of aging:

Do we have any real influence in the matter?

Can we slow it down?

Can we stop it?

Can we even reverse it?

Listen to your body reactions as you contemplate such questions. This is the status of your belief system today. You are looking directly into the face of your limitations.

How does your body respond to these questions?

Do they sit easily in your tissues.....or do you rumble with discomfort to your very core?

Note well both the quality and quantity of your bodily responses to each question.

Where do you draw the line on this issue?

And just what might that line be?

We are talking of possibilities and limitations. Could you accept a maybe in answer to each of the questions? Could you accept something a little stronger? How about the possibility of a yes to every one of them?

How does your system respond if you contemplate the possibility that an accurate answer might not be so much of a yes as a **Yes Indeed,** in deed, in fact, and in truth!?

How does *that* sit in your tissues?

The following must be fully understood, for it is a truth that underlies our work:

Not only are bodies changeable, they represent change itself. They are more of a process than they are a thing. Bodies exist in a state of change...as a state of change. At any given moment their morphology is no more than the sum total of all the demands then being placed on them. (Even if many of today's demands are only memories of yesterday's misunderstandings.)

If you would change the body then change the demands on that body. Even the demands of your expectations! It's imperative that this be understood, for we can not allow ourselves to accept artificial limitations upon our work.

As a step toward freedom then, examine now this dynamic structure of your own, this form that lives in a constant state of adaptation to a dynamic world.

Consider the following points:

This body that you are wearing today, just what does it say about you?

Does it present a message?

Is it a clear and unclouded message?

Does it match your intentions of how you would like to be perceived by the world?

Of what limitations does it speak?

Of what limitations does it try not to speak?

Does it move and behave as you would wish it to?

Does it moan and groan?

What would you most like to change about this structure......and how might you go about that?

Departure possibilities......

If you were to work on your own body, where might you begin the process?

The body harbours such a multitude of intriguing sights, each contesting for attention, each a potential embarcadero.

Of primary concern here is that now we are looking for secrets, and secrets thrive on illusion.

But they do leave footprints. Tracks that we can visualize in the physical structure of the body, as well as in its functioning, visualize in all the movements that pass through or around that structure.

Reflecting upon this apparent duality of structure and function you will realize that actually you are considering two aspects of the same event. The structural event adds shape and potential to the functional side, while function helps define structural possibilities. It's a curiously circular relationship. Change either one and you automatically change the other. Focusing your attention on either will help you recognize the tracks of the other.

As the client enters your office he is even then in the process of change. It's your job to orchestrate the direction and the shape of changes that are already in progress.

The **rationale** behind whatever actions you choose to take can be considered on any of the multiple levels in which we work. One choice might be to focus your attention on the biochemical situation.

When bodily processes function properly, their functioning is collectively referred to as Physiology. When the very same processes go awry, their functioning is labeled Pathology. So we may view what is so quickly and definitively called Pathology as only Physiology out of sync.

On this level, our working principle might be that as we change the structure, we are also changing its functioning. With each shift in any configuration of the physical form there comes a corresponding shift in its physiology. The more stress released from the functioning of a structure the more energy that becomes available for a more efficient life.

If we further consider any physical malfunctioning as a behavioral pattern, we can understand why our work is so applicable in such a diversity of situations.

So then, what do you **feel** about the practical limits governing the effectiveness of your work?

Not as a political/legal consideration, but as a practical application, might bodywork influence the course of any given situation? Possibly every situation?

The answer for me, is that quite possibly it might. There are certainly suggestions to be found in abundance for this to be the case.

That's my establishment answer, my conservative answer that keeps me out of trouble! The truth is that I have witnessed too many of what some call miracles to seriously question their existence any longer!

It's just a matter of remembering some basics:

*Whatever the level, and whatever the aspect of any situation that we might hope to influence, the process really begins and ends within the boundaries established by the attitudinal framework that we share with our client.

*This body of our client holds all the answers within. It's our job to create a physical climate where that body feels safe enough for the sharing of its secrets.

*We do this by letting the tissues feel our respect...so that we may engage their curiosity...and then their trust.

There is something more to know about the character of the tissues we are concerned with. It's an aspect of the soul we are dealing with here, an aspect that appears to hold its secrets very dearly. But the truth is that deep within every mass of tissue resides the vestige of a first class gossip. It may be a closet gossip to be sure...but it's a gossip nonetheless.

Once the tissues understand our respect and our interest, their hearts may open up to us, they may snuggle up... tissue to tissue...soul to soul...and pour out their little secrets.

The soul knows:

"The truth shall set you free"...

.......and tissues never lie!

Curious Tales.............

.....and Pitfalls of the Road

I've heard a lot of loose talk about this yellow brick road lately. I've heard curious tales of physical transformations altering the course of lives, I've heard rumours of personal powers claimed that previously were not even imagined. I've heard the stories everywhere, at the beach, in the hot tubs and the saunas...wherever people who are wont to talk of such things tend to gather.

I've overheard wonderous tales that seem to ride the winds through the corridors and out the windows and into the streets. Wonderous tales certainly....and yet there seems to be an elusive and tantalizingly vague quality about each of them, as if they speak more of a dream of Xanadu than of a reality in the 20th Century.

We've all been exposed in varying degrees to the undercurrents of such yarns but how much of what we hear is exaggeration and how much fact? What might we encounter if we dare to look behind the facade, directly into the face of our mythological dreams?

What is illusion and what is reality on this road?
What are the practical possibilities here?

Who are all these people and why are they walking this path in the first place?

More to the point, if my life is working for me right now, why should I even consider joining such a questionable crowd?

Underlying all these questions is yet another question. An even more basic question that can answer all the other questions. It's so simple and so obvious, how can it be that it is so often left unasked by so many bodyworkers?

What can this road do for you? Well, what exactly would you like from this, your road?

What would you change about your present situation if you had a magic wish?

What would you like to create, recreate, or remove from your life? Care to go in search of your soul?

What exactly might your most secret and delicious pleasure be?

Remember that as healers we hold dual citizenship. While playing the role of bodyworker, hesitate a bit and consider both aspects and reflect that such a question may be of some importance to the client. These sessions do belong to her you know! It's flagrantly inconsiderate of us to blithely begin the proceedings without even taking that little extra time necessary to consult her dreams.

Along this road we learn to design unique sessions to match the unique wants and unique needs of absolutely unique clients.

It's implicit in the contract of course that, as body changes occur, goal changes will not lag far behind and as tissues release their restrictions the client will be able to see and contemplate new options. As she watches her impossibles evolve into her obtainables, she might opt to go exploring among the varied landscapes throughout the kingdom of Easy. She might distance herself from past experiences, up the ante and go for total freedom from the bondage of whatever past she carries with her. She may pursue the ecstasy of living completely in present time.

Consider her choices, which are legion. Ours is a roadway of abundance. There is no shortage of systems from which to choose, and each brings with it its own unique vision of glory. So many systems...of so many varieties...so many possibilities to explore.

Clients!

Before entering this road listen to the voices of the systems for they speak with eloquence. **Listen**...and hear the promise and the prophecy.

Listen how they offer you **balance** in one form or another. It doesn't really matter which aspect of balance they focus on, because balance is a function of the system as a whole. All of our spirit/mind/body aspects are totally interdependent. This is that ocean upon which no island can exist in isolation. Here each is an inseparable member of the community. It's impossible to speak to any one characteristic of the body without at least nudging all the others.

Listen to the voices that promise an increased **awareness** of the self. A goal to be highly esteemed and certainly worthy of pursuit. A goal that inevitably leads to a more complete recognition of the self...of the true self...which leads inescapably to the release of chronic muscular tensions...which constitutes a not inconsiderable portion of our holding patterns.

Which is well along on the roadway to **ease,** which is a very nice place to visit and even to live. Ease too, comes in various sizes and shapes and each of them is family. There is ease of the body and ease of the spirit, ease with the universe, and ease with the gravitational field...which all too often is incorrectly perceived as oppressive. This land of Ease is both large and productive and its chief export is Comfort.

Listen to the voices and you may choose to pursue **enlightenment.** Now there's a goal for you! No messing around here. And like its relatives ease and balance, enlightenment too is multifaceted. Mental, physical, spiritual enlightenment, take your choice, or go for the package.

You may also notice that almost every system at least alludes to the element of **grace**...if they don't talk about it outright. There is certainly no shortage of talk on this road, especially from the more organized bodywork systems. **It's all such big talk and it's all true!** Systems can deliver on their promises. If they say they can do it, they can do it...usually.

Every one of their postulations is available, and more, by a factor of X at the very least. As wonderous as this might sound, the outlandish possibilities remain as yet unspoken. No matter what your desired destination, there is some brand of bodywork somewhere that can ease your path.

However, it's not all roses on this road, the verbiage itself creates an element of chaos. All the bodywork systems share a similar terminology that creates a certain confusion in our ranks.

There are so many diverse systems, and so many independent practitioners who work outside of the systems, and they all claim to work toward the same ends but turn out such vastly different products.

Inconsistencies which may be no more than the placing of an emphasis on different aspects of the same goal. Or possibly it's a case of the terminology not matching the actions, but there are inconsistencies nevertheless. The point is to be aware that different systems do get different results, despite sharing a common pool of rhetoric.

So look more at what they do rather than what they say, noting particularly what the norm is throughout a system. Specific results may often be more a function of the individual practitioner than of the system as a whole.

Rhetoric notwithstanding, bodywork is fundamentally a partnered dance in which the parameters of what can be artistically accomplished are shaped as much by the form of the dance as by its participants.

In fact, the most significant limitation to artistic expression may come through its form, its context. Just as modern dance has a different set of limitations than classical ballet, so it is with bodywork. The form of our dance is to be found within the system and, as great as any form may be, strict adherence to it may ultimately become a factor of limitation.

As a prospective client how important is all this to me on a practical level?

Which is just another way to ask the question of what bodywork can do for you...and there are better ways to ask the question.

What do you factually want from your bodywork?

If you can get it, can you handle it?

How much of your energy are you willing to commit to this project?

Make no mistake about it......**all the stories are true!** All those gut-bursting, reality-busting results are available, but they do demand your participation as well as your emotional commitment.

The commitment is to Change, which wraps itself within an interesting mantle. Change equals the unknown, which often emits a disturbing quality that is reminiscent of your first encounter with a haunted house...complete with squeaky door and thunderstorm...at midnight on Halloween. It tends to scare the living bejesus out of the ego.

It may seem amusing while surrounded by all the familiar creature comforts to intellectually consider what might lie just behind that door over to the left...but this is not contemplation we are talking about here...it is certainly not the familiar...and it may not even be the comfortable.

Here we are on the move! This is where we leave the home and the family and the friends behind. This is where we drop the speculation and dance head-on into those murky shadows that eclipse all of our personal inconceivabilities.

To the compressed ego this promises to be a bone chilling experience. Our unknowns certainly would not have remained unexplored and unknown for so long unless there were some good reasons behind it!

You do have some options here. You could just as easily make the journey completely lighthearted, a lark, or a smashing adventure story, for most likely you will encounter such diverse elements all along the way.

And before the music starts and the dance begins consider this: It's more than just helpful if both parties are clear on the line of dance, on the direction in which they are going to proceed...it's essential. Which means that once again we are speaking about your prerogatives as client.

Bodyworkers...
There may be wavering sunsets ahead. Remember that this tends to be a road full of convoluted surprises. Don't be shocked if your client's goals shrink into the extremely forgettable, or expand across as-yet uncharted horizons. Such events occur as the reality of change becomes fully apparent to the client. Her interests may shift focus...or be abandoned completely. It's not all that rare for a client to experience an overwhelming need to stay exactly where she finds herself at the moment.

Nor is it uncommon to find clients who like to play at change, while keeping the ego luxury of not actually letting go of the comforts that come with the territory of a staunchly fixed position. When such a client discovers genuine movement taking place her bewildered ego may go into shock. There was nothing like this in the original contract!

On one occasion I was offered an incredible amount of money to put a client back exactly the way he was when he first stepped into my office.

Impossible! That was seven weeks ago. That was history. We can't retrace our footsteps...not with any success we can't. Our behavior patterns are incredibly complicated affairs, the result of countless life experiences that have become stuck in our tissues under very specific emotional time and space considerations.

With this particular client, bodywork had released some incompletely experienced traumas from their cellular prisons. Even their footprints were erased...and were no longer retrievable.

It was equally impossible to relive all the original experiences that had established the pattern in the first place. Nor could my client approximate his familiar but lost patterns of behavior with any degree of success.

When this client first entered my office he was easily the most volatile human I had ever encountered. The smell of danger oozed from his cells. He reeked of an ill-concealed hostility that was perceived by everyone as so potentially dangerous that whenever he entered a room even those who didn't see his entrance were immediately aware of his presence.

He had no friends and never did have. His body was a walking defense against intimacy. But his presence was never, ever ignored. Which was very pleasing to his ego image.

These old patterns of his had sheltered the ego from the frightening risk of intimate contact and, once the secrets that imprisoned these patterns were gone, his ego defenses were no longer so forbidding. Perfect strangers came right up to him and made sociable overtures and didn't even have sense enough to be nervous about it.

Such audacity!...and what was worse very few even bothered to notice when he entered a room.

Friendly overtures were bad enough, but being ignored was the most humiliating experience of all. His ego just wasn't ready to deal with such an insulting turn of events. His old world had fallen completely to pieces and his ego wanted no part of this new one. All these pushy stimulations and possibilities were just too frightening to an already overfrightened ego.

And now his shadow gently rocks my soul whenever I am tempted to value words more than tissues.

He is an example of one who would rather be comfortable within the confines of his carefully constructed cage than actually leave its familiar security. There are many like him out there. With them our immediate goal may be just to help them tidy up their boxes a bit.

Such clients are seldom aware of the limiting effect of their attitudes as they start their processing. They badly underestimate the awesome potential of bodywork.

On this road the obvious is often not so obvious. The curves and surprises come in a continuing series. Clients will come into your offices so busy defending what they have that there is simply no space available for even the slightest fundamental alteration.

This becomes obvious to the bodyworker before it does the client. Although they come to you asking for change, you will be able to sense that, on some deeper level, they see change as threatening to the immortality of the ego.

It's crucial that we understand the client's interest in our work. We must be alert to those who want only to loosen up within the bounds of their present structures and have no real interest in substantially changing those structures...they do have a certain familiarity with their boundaries, and after all these boundaries have gotten them this far...so with these we must consider the work as only a tune up, not a major overhaul.

This is a legitimate framework in which to do our work. We need only to recognize the context we are working in, and remember that goals are usually renegotiable somewhere down the line. When we respect what is present we create a climate of comfort that invites even the most entrenched rigidities to take an occasional break.

With the best of intentions....

There is yet another mechanism for the client to consider. This is the extremely unsettling effect that substantial changes in her may have on her circle of friends.

Change in one member of a group all too often becomes a threat to the others. It has all the appearances of a betrayal, an unspoken agreement that has been breached, and in a sense it is. The lie of individual non-responsibility has been illuminated and the myth of personal helplessness exposed.

Once we acknowledge the possibility of change on a very fundamental level, then we can no longer avoid a nagging sense of personal responsibility and, what has even more awesome implications, of individual accountability. Which may lead to the recognition that each of us is truly the architect of his own body and ultimately of his own world. An admission that could very well be the end of that world as it now stands.

Somehow, on some level, all members of the group sense their common danger. It's easier to overlook the changes, or to disapprove of them, or even to sabotage them if they can.

"Don't you think you've lost enough weight now, dear."

Crossroads.....

The range of possibilities inherent within good body-work can be a bit disquieting at times. We must face the possibility of living in this world in a totally new and different manner. The possibility of surrendering our beloved positions and living without defense and without being "right."

Who knows what the consequences of living such a life might be...a life without struggle? If efforting has nothing to do with achieving goals, what effect might this have on our well indoctrinated egos?

Body Secrets

What if we really don't have to live within the rigid confines of our upbringing? What if we can live up to all of our original capabilities? What if there is no need at all to beat ourselves up or to feel guilty about something we have or haven't done.....what then?

A surprise awaits just ahead. As you contact your original self, your innocent self, you will find you are not at all who you thought you were. There is *more* of you available than you ever imagined there was, and it's only a matter of letting go, of releasing limitations, of allowing your own natural rhythms to sweep your tissues clean.

You may have been holding on to a particular thought about yourself or about your place in the universe. You may have been holding yourself back or holding yourself in or holding yourself yourself up or even holding yourself together...but whatever you have been holding you can let it go. Whatever thoughts you have about yourself, you can let them go too. If you have to hold it, it's already passé.

You are always more than what you hold....and it's impossible to find your innocence locked in the rigid embrace of an ego defense.

Nor can you encounter yourself in your present time physical shape. You are always in a continual process of shaping and reshaping yourself anyway. Right this moment you may be in your shape or out of your shape, but whatever your physical or emotional or financial shape...you transcend them all.

This is what you are not!

What you are is potential. Pure and unlimited potential...available potential just sitting and waiting for you to stake your claim and your tools of choice can be found scattered all along this Yellow Brick Road.

If you can dream it you can claim it.

All your original dreams are still waiting faithfully, still hoping to catch your eye, still yours for the asking.

Your dream may be of a new sensitivity to your inner workings, possibly an early warning system that alerts you to dangers of the ego before even a solitary tissue barrier settles in place, an awareness that screams at the slightest trace of the coming of the dreaded Position, screams before it's able to dig its defensive trenches. Utopian literature accurately considers such awareness as a pre-condition for living fully in the Now.

Your dream may be of removing whatever barriers there are between you and your higher self and, from this perspective, moving into a more easy relationship with every aspect of your environment.

Every aspect! Your dream may blanket the entire range of human experience, covering all the possibilities.

It doesn't matter that you may have been living in cramped inner spaces. Bodywork can expand your spaces to meet your potential. It can help you remove your labels. Labels which may even have been true for you at one time...but understand that your labels are your limitations...and it's equally as true that you are more than your labels. Which is also about claiming your potential.

Clients continually instruct me about the potentials and possibilities of this work. They are my most profound teachers, those who come to receive, and then take the time to help me more properly understand the nature of the road we travel together.

As I watch them overtaking their dreams, all that I once considered the logical limitations of bodywork is torn asunder. What I once considered the impossible, I now look upon as just another of my private limitations, just one more possibility to consider and possibly pursue.

An understanding of the mechanical details of the process doesn't really matter very much. It doesn't even matter if I can offer a reasonable explanation for what it is that happens.

What is important is that I get my beliefs out of the way, listen to the body before me, and allow the events to have their say. Results speak loudly enough for themselves. When a problem is solved, no additional comments are really necessary.

The possibility and the dream exist within each other. Unfortunately, when the dream moves into the realm of probability the emerging grace and freedom of a now unfamiliar body may be perceived as confusing and frightening. Movements without familiar limitations may be viewed as motion gone out of control, we may label it "clumsy" and distance ourselves from it.

It is interesting to note, however, that those who most actively pursue the graceful life, the professional dancers, are the very ones who most welcome this new movement.

They know the experience for what it is. They never call it clumsy.

They call it by its proper name: **Opportunity.**

But for those who prefer the security of a familiar and well delineated structure, such expanding limits can be a mite disturbing. The slightest crack in their walls may trigger a quiet panic. Sometimes not so quiet. Our equation must also take this into consideration.

Go easy with these not-so-intrepid warriors for they are the ones who have forgotten the taste of freedom, forgotten what an incredibly heady wine it really is. Or possibly they never even knew.

Freedoms previously untasted can lead us to all manner of unique and exotic discoveries...as much about the self as about the world...and just as you are not the self you thought you were, the world is not the world you thought it was. If not one and the same, you and your world are at least mutually interdependent.

As exciting as this prospect might sound, you ain't heard nothing yet! The best is all to come. Because possibly, just possibly, the ultimate aim of bodywork is to help you contact that element of divinity that resides within each of us. Possibly all the other work that went before was only in preparation for this incredibly awesome moment of recognition. Which must be the ultimate! ....or so I thought.

But as much as I relish the overwhelming ecstasy that lives within that eternal moment of discovery, my present understanding is that this is where the real bodywork begins.....

This is no more than the start of the yellow brick road...only the beginning of the dream.

A Quick Two-Step

A few problems.........a little background...

There is wonder in this profession of ours. We work in a constant process of discovery where latent potentials continually blossom before our eyes. But as satisfying as the work itself is, the semantics surrounding it present us with an occasional problem. Even the category itself is perceived as foggy around the edges...and justifiably so.

How does one go about looking up bodywork in the yellow pages? Exactly who is included under this heading?

Seldom do we get the separate listing we deserve and we seem to transcend whatever category we find ourselves in. Should we be listed with the Holistic Health Services?

Absolutely!

Alternative Medicine?

We belong there.

Aren't we covered under the umbrella of Massage?

There too.

But each of these headings is a restriction, a compression on us. It's a matter of semantics. The problem is that limitation always comes with definition and our field itself is unlimited. **Our work is as much a manual medicine for the soul as it is for the body.**

It's tempting to be seduced by the familiarity of "hands-on therapy," but this too implies another artificial limitation. Physical healings continually take place all around the world without the requirement of flesh-to-flesh contact. Healing energy is as often as not transmitted in the absence of a direct physical connection. Some may try to subdivide this aspect of our work into the separate category of "psychic healing" but that too has all the elements of bodywork.

If there is one central factor to distinguish the field, it is probably the therapeutic use of **all** the human energies, whatever form the transmission might take.

Bodywork is first of all a therapeutic discipline in the grandest and most natural sense. The holistic viewpoint of health identifies disease as a condition where the patient is out of ease, out of balance, and out of harmony with all about him. All the exact elements directly addressed by the bodyworker.

While this designation of Bodyworker is fairly recent, our practices and concepts certainly are not. The natural tradition of healing has always been quietly present, even within the western world.

Voltaire, for example, had his priorities in order. More than two hundred years ago he observed that healing was the art of amusing the patient while nature cured the disease.

And Benjamin Franklin noted that, while it was God who heals, it was the doctor who took the fee.

These two understood healing principles and practices, as did Thomas Edison who predicted that the doctor of the future would give no medicine, but would interest his clients in the care of their structures as well as their diets and in the causes and preventions of disease.

Three timeless voices of reason, and while they didn't stand alone, they clearly swam against the popular tide of Modern Medicine. Three voices that most assuredly would welcome the inclusion of bodyworkers into the field of health care.

Professional medicine men, unfortunately, have not always been so open. There has been an historical hesitancy for health professionals to refer patients outside of their own license.

In modern times the medics held the franchise and placed themselves above and separate from the Chiropractors and the Osteopaths and the Naturopaths and the Naprapaths and the Nutritionists and all the other assorted healers. They even tried, and almost succeeded, in absorbing the Osteopaths whole. The health system was a closed and exclusive club, even if somewhat frayed around the edges. If you were sick and sensible and scientific-minded you submitted yourself to medical experts and that was that.

But not quite...there were cracks in the system and sometimes, here and there, a patient slipped through.

The scenario played like this: of all those the medics could not help, there were some who refused to sit quietly and accept their fate, some who didn't just give up in frustration after tramping from one medical authority to another, some who continued looking got lucky and found their way into one of the alternative healing arts, possibly Chiropractic, and there, despite what the medics had told them about Chiropractors, they got often spectacular results, results that at times bordered on the miraculous.

Such goings-on can not go completely unnoticed for long. And today referrals between these two groups are not as uncommon as they once were, in California at least, which always seems to be ahead of the rest of the world by a few years anyway. This may not yet be the practice of the majority, but it does seem to be the trend.

And now there's a more modern version of this old scenario which casts bodyworkers in the role that Chiropractors used to occupy. This time the patient who is unable to find satisfaction from either the Medics or the Chiropractors finds his way to a bodyworker. And it's not so much a matter of pure chance anymore either.

It was not that long ago when only the occasional doctor who called himself holistic would dare refer outside his speciality. Now the number of cross referring professionals grows daily and an ever increasing number of holistic health centers include bodyworkers on their staff.

Credit for this healthy trend is due primarily to the specialty of sports medicine, where the consumers are high tech performers who are exceptionally well acquainted with the machinery of their bodies.

They are biomechanical experts in the pursuit of maximum efficiency and are less interested in philosophy or union affiliations than in results.

They demand the same high quality from their health care services that they do from themselves. The fallout from their quest for excellence reverberates throughout the entire spectrum of health care services.

The bottom line......

When the body has a physical problem it is termed a **lesion,** and is defined as: "any pathological or traumatic discontinuity of tissue or loss of function of a part." **Loss of function and discontinuity.**

The body functions as a unit, and as a unit will exhibit the consequences of a lesion, no matter where that lesion may originate. A painful shoulder may make itself known anywhere throughout the territory and is capable of influencing the entire scope of body mechanics. The pain may originate in the shoulder, or be reflected to the shoulder from some other location. But it is seldom as ingenuous as it might at first appear.

The original lesion can hide but it always leaves its spoor: compressed tissues causing compacted and cogwheel-type micromovements that insure a residual heritage of biomechanical inefficiency.

A compressed body is an inefficient body, a body not working to maximum efficiency. A shortened and rigid muscle unit is well on its way to bankruptcy, its movement allowance has been squandered.

In the efficient muscle unit, contraction is closely followed by relaxation, leaving the body once again in a state of alert; capable of continuing action and reaction, which is the portrait of a relaxed body, which just happens to equate with a healthy body, with a body living close to its capabilities.

In its natural state of alert relaxation a body is also able to accelerate its own healing processes significantly. Whatever the injury, whatever the condition, recovery time will be noticeably shortened in a balanced body.

Bodyworkers understand all this about the body and attend not only to the actual lesion, but to each of its reflections as well. We promote whole body efficiency through relaxed and balanced movement. Our concern is with **function and continuity.** Obviously then, bodywork must be considered an essential element of comprehensive sports medicine care.

But with the category so blurred, how does one connect with bodywork in the absence of a personal referral?

Well, the systems do have a way of making themselves known, and there are certainly a multitude of good systems from which to choose. New names are continually entering the field which is all to the good for with each new system comes new concepts and new possibilities. It's only a question of preference.

It's never a question of which is the best system per se,

but which is the best system for you. You and the system, a relationship in which the most important ingredient is the **you.** Of vital importance is how well you resonate with the system. It's always a matter of selecting the system most appropriate to your needs.

The systems draw from a common pool of rhetoric, so occasionally their goals and their processes sound the same, but their results expose the inaccuracies of the language. Bodyworkers combine and recombine the same words in a noble effort to say the unsayable.

Appreciate if you will how difficult it is, if not actually impossible, to accurately verbalize this process of bodywork. This is human growth, life itself, we are talking about here. How can one squeeze so unique an experience into the confines of a language?

People who know their way around the bodywork scene often ask me to be precise about whatever it is that I do, and my answers sound suspiciously like those of everyone else in the field. We all tend to use similar words even when our tools and our results may differ radically.

There is **a rip off** here. Our similarity of language keeps prospective clients separate from the wonderous possibilities available to them because they have already sampled the rhetoric and, with that particular pairing, it just didn't work for them.

It's the other side of the problem for the prospective bodyworker looking for a system to study. Teachers of bodywork, in or out of a system, all sound like they teach the same process.

Fortunately for us all, this is a self selecting field. Those that produce quality in their work, endure. Those that don't, fold up and move on. So when considering body-work look to their track records. If they are prospering and have been around awhile it's probably because of good results.

Each system has enough of value within it to warrant our studying as many of them as possible, in as much depth as possible. Each system was founded on some gem of great truth which, mixed with all the other gems of great truth of all the other systems, may begin to approximate the unique truths to be found within any individual client of yours.

While pursuing the truth within each system just beware of the Dogma that surrounds it. The very same Dogma that may ultimately turn the system into its own worst enemy. The Dogma that locks the system into rigid parameters which dictate the scope and shape of all future input.

There are systems that hold onto their Dogma as if their very existence depends on it. They have become confused about their identity, forgetting that any system will always evolve into more than its founding doctrines.

And there are schools that even claim to be absolutely unique in what they do, producing exclusive results that are not to be found in any other bodyworker outside of that system. This is only a rhetorical statement that, under the circumstances, is to be expected. It's really only a logical extension of Dogma.

There does appear to be an increasing number of exceptions to this practice. Such self destructive tendencies appear to be on the ebb...even if a few schools still maintain rigid requirements for training that restrict their system to bringing in newcomers who are just like the ones already in the system, thereby producing a set of clones that may be flattering to the selection committee, but do little to encourage progress within the system.

Those who fancy themselves as the elite always seem to know the least about the other techniques that are available to them, a shortsightedness which cheats them as much as it does their clientele.

If it should happen that you apply for bodywork training and are denied admission, don't take it seriously.

Do not consider anyone else's assessment of your potential as having any final validity.

Be sure to attend to their words closely and learn from them certainly, but understand that the selection process may be primarily a self serving ritual.

There are countless successful bodyworkers who have been told by one system or another that they just didn't have the necessary qualities to do the work. That they were just not the right physical or intellectual or emotional type to be a bodyworker. I have met quite a few who did not accept their sentence and now rank among the most effective bodyworkers practicing.

There is an arrogance in such a selection process that is an affront to our entire profession. Possibly the only legitimate requirements for training may be the desire to do the work and a commitment to liberating the bodyworker that lives within us all.

Yet I hear criticism, usually expressed on moral grounds, about the supposedly easy admission policies of a few schools. The fear seems to be that the wrong sort of person will become a bodyworker and wreak havoc on the public. This has failed to happen. I see no drop in either the abilities or the ethics of graduates from these schools.

What I do see throughout the field are individual practitioners transcending their training...or their lack of it.

There is really no cause for concern here, the work has a self limiting factor about it, and the more of us there are, the more competition there is, the better results we need just to stay in business. The inefficient and the unethical are elbowed out, improving the situation for all of us.

Heaven knows, the world can certainly use as many good bodyworkers as it can get. An urgent and clear social priority is the improvement of relations between different segments of our planet. Which includes improving relationships between the different bodywork systems themselves.

The point to be considered is that every relationship, of any kind, involves at least some element of bodywork in it. The more people doing the work then the better off we are both as individuals and as a society.

A Quick Two-Step

As a Very Reliable Source once said:

"If you bring forth what is within you
    what you bring forth will save you.

If you do not bring forth what is within you
    what you do not bring forth will destroy you."

* * * * * *

Jesus
The Gospel of Thomas
Gnostic Gospels

The Systems........
........and Beyond

"Wow! You look great! What are you doing these days?"

"I'm getting rolfed!" .....and so it starts.

Bodywork became known by word of mouth, satisfied clients proselytizing to their friends. And in the early days the name of a popular system was most often used in the generic sense, representing the entire profession.

Today bodywork is more widely known, more accepted as a unique field of specialization within itself. Several of its systems are currently being practiced throughout the world.

There is an international fraternity of bodyworkers that, even though fragmented and poorly connected, remains a fraternity nevertheless. Their work binds them together. Some of them associate loosely through the methodology of a given system, while even more pursue their craft outside of any formal organizational framework.

These latter practitioners work without the luxury of associating with an established system. And a luxury it is, a shelter providing the comforts of a proven formula with the security of fairly predictable results. The novice automatically assumes the reputation of the system as a whole and is perceived by the public as a known quantity. His entry into professional life is eased by this pre-established reputation.

The pull of a system is doubly seductive to the beginner. With the security of a recipe to follow there is far less possibility of losing your way, after all you do have a roadmap to follow.

As comforting as this may sound, the framework of a system is not essential for either functional or financial success. The majority of practicing bodyworkers are independents. Every area produces its own indigenous practitioners whose work quite often originates with them.

While seldom well known outside of their own province, their work is effective by any standard you care to apply. Their work may have been handed down from within the family and it may be passed on the same way, or taught to a single apprentice outside the family, or to no one at all, in which case the work still stands as a foundation for subsequent bodyworkers in the area to build upon.

It is possible to learn our trade through awareness, observation and trial and error, although this is neither the easiest nor the quickest way. Good training is available through a great variety of sources. Schools and apprenticeship situations abound. Just be aware that some very good schools carry a very heavy price tag: an exclusive commitment to their form of the work. If you become confronted with a dilemma such as this, just remember that your first obligation is to yourself and to your art.

Systems may appear to be much the same, to be mirror reflections of one another with superficial nips and tucks taken here and there for cosmetic purposes, but that's on the surface. At the nucleus of each system there is a special and unique quality that makes it what it is and, while it might be tempting to liken one system to another, that would neither please nor be fair to either of them.

And it's never a question of one system being better than another. All statements of this sort are just self-serving rhetoric. The truth is that established practitioners within every system use whatever techniques that work best for them personally, no matter where those techniques might originate.

Systemic rhetoric is propagated by the purist, of which each school has its share. They can be easily recognized by their intrepid shouts of "no compromise!" Stout fellows all, they follow a common script. Five years of practice and either they burn out and quit, or their work settles into a predictable mediocrity.

Their results are still consistent and still beneficial, but their work has become dated. They have chosen to keep the faith and remain steady while all about them the world and their craft passes them by.

They are the paradox of our profession. Our specialty is change, but these keep themselves constant and unchanging. *They have removed themselves from the equation.*

Rote repetition, years of practicing the same moves over and over again, does not guarantee mastery......Not in a living art like ours it doesn't.

Just compare these practitioners with newcomers who enter the field radiating enthusiasm, intuitive to the process, and welcoming an unobstructed flow of information. These stand on the shoulders of all who have gone before and, because of their flexible attitude, their work tends to be effective from the very beginning and never remains static thereafter but improves from session to session. Bodyworkers such as these are their own best tools; essential elements in a successful bodywork formula.

As you evaluate either a system or an individual bodyworker, keep this principle in mind and weight the attitude at least as importantly as the experience.

There is yet another myth that says you have to specialize in just one system in order to become a proficient bodyworker. This is not only completely untrue but completely contraindicated as well! The artists within each system are always familiar with other systems and borrow from them as well...even if covertly. The truth is, if you are knowledgeable in only one system then you don't really know that system at all.

The study of the body from any unfamiliar frame of reference will illuminate unsuspected corners of your own technique.

There is great benefit for every professional in studying within a system. And after practicing that system for a while, there is even more benefit in going out and learning a second system, being careful, of course, not to discard anything from the first.

Whatever the name of the systems, they are never incompatible.

That is only a would-be magical chant, so recognize it for what it is, a myth of separation and poverty.

One body of knowledge is not meant to supplant another. One never subtracts from its brother. Each new system or technique only adds to the aggregate. **When faced with seeming incompatibilities, just take a step back and expand into a larger perspective.** As you adapt to a view that accommodates more information, the benefits will be amply and immediately reflected in the quality of your work.

Every system that has stood the test of time has a proven value. At its very worst it may just be inappropriate in a given situation, maybe not even inappropriate, just not the most appropriate one available. Working exclusively within a single system is like running an obstacle course with blinders on. It limits your vision as well as your options.

Most organized techniques originate from a single source, and no matter who or how fine that source is, this too tends to become a limiting factor. Some will argue that this single source insures quality control. I have found just the opposite to be true, that continual growth and quality are best insured through input from multiple sources, with equal weight conceded to each. The teacher must also learn from the student, which insures that the system will remain strong and expanding.

There is also the matter of The Recipe to consider, which is usually the backbone of a system. It is often both the foundation and the strength of that system, but it may just as easily become a weakness from within. A good recipe carries an inherent time bomb with it, the tendency of its followers to rigidify and/or deify the process. Which ultimately becomes detrimental to the health of the system, not to mention the practitioner and the client.

The recipe may be just too good. It may produce such predictably fine results that at any given moment, your attention will be more on the application of the recipe than on the needs of your client. You may be so immersed in the application that you don't even notice those fleeting whispers that timidly nudge at the corner of your soul and, if you do notice them, they may not coincide exactly with your formula.

Where the murmur and the formula conflict, the easiest path is the most familiar path and with a recipe to rely on one is not so quick to follow an unpredictable course into the unknown. The formula tends to become a security blanket.

But the magic comes in following the client along whatever pathway her tissues may choose. It's just possible that she may lead us to the galaxies...even to that storied pathway of veiled wonders itself, which may be waiting for us just behind the mist, obscured only by our faintness of heart.

Where the soul and the recipe intersect, the essential requirement is the courage to run with your client directly into the unknown. This is neither the time for timidity nor for a formula!

If anything the formula is seductive. The client benefits, we get our applause, and we stay on safe ground.

The recipe soon comes to assume its own importance. It becomes known as The Work and creates its own mystique. It is then too important to be put into writing where the uninitiated could gain easy access to it. God Forbid! Who knows what they might do with it!

When it does occasionally slip out of the closet and into print, it becomes an inspirational source of illumination for many of our more isolated brothers and sisters of bodywork.

Ida Rolf birthed just such a magnificent formula on which so many subsequent systems are based. But working with such a powerful instrument it becomes increasingly easy to lose sight of the totality of our client. Specifically with those peculiar rhythms not in complete harmony with our formula. We can bend our client, we can mold her, we can fit her to our model, but in the process we may lose some of her unique and precious peculiarities. We may unwittingly bury the very key we are looking for.

This is the trap inherent in following a single system. It's all laid out for you. Its obvious efficiency can lure you into an easy complacency. You get good results and there is a fine end product that tends to create a climate of certainty.

You know what your system can do. Given time and experience this certainty tends to become absolute. The danger is that we then know all we will ever need to know about working on a body. The system works exactly as it is. After all you don't mess with success.

Such absolute certainty is absolutely incompatible with the unique current of truth that flows through the client. Certainty interferes with the free flow of information which effectively limits where you can go and what possibly may be just as important, how you can get there.

An attitude of certainty comes from having final answers and knowing that you have them. Systems do have remarkably good answers....but an inbred quality of answers is that they interfere with the questioning process itself. They tend to cut short the investigation, which proves ultimately to be of the greatest value. It's through this process that clients are able to uncover and incorporate their own unique truths into their own unique systems.

We serve them best by allowing them to unwrap their own secrets at their own rates layer by layer, and in so doing erasing all vestiges of them forever.

This is empowerment!

Use all the tools available, from whatever the source. There are several systems of knowledge that can help you immensely in interpreting what the body is trying to tell you. They detail with great clarity a link between a certain part of the body and a specific life situation.

A weakness in your lower legs, for instance, may represent a weakness in your support system while a stiff neck or a pain in the butt, may be comments on your attitudes or your companions. At other levels the same murmurs may represent, respectively, a hesitancy to move, an inflexibility, or problems with personal power.

They are all comments that are accurate, unusually accurate. They tell of a connection well beyond chance probability, of a relationship much more than coincidental. This is practical and useful information, and an excellent place to begin your exploration.

But only to begin, never to end the investigation. Use everything that's available, but use it as a guide....not as a Bible. With this particular client, whatever generic guide-lines you use may no longer be the most accurate or the most essential elements. Meanings are not obliged to re-main attached to a specific area forever. The original mean-ing may be overridden and shift with the circumstances of life. These indicators are neither a constant, nor an absolute. Precise at one point in time, they may become inappropriate at another. Layers of meaning may have been added, shuf-fled, and reassembled.

Maximal results depend upon the recognition that

every individual is always just that, a complete individual. Each carries a unique form, created by a unique history, which tends to modify pre-existing patterns and create new and original connections.

Accepting the dictates of any system without question, to the exclusion of all others, may mislead and eventually sabotage the entire investigative process. There is an abundance of useful information available to us, so we must definitely consider it all, but only as possibilities. We are at our most effective when we **explore** the possibilities with our client, rather than dictate them to her.

It is ultimately a matter of ethics and integrity. Ethics demand that we respect the integrity of our client. There can be no short cuts. If we play Experts and herald for her all the significant factors that underlie her areas of blocked energy, there is the danger that she may believe us, and that would be too bad for it might cut short what is arguably the most important aspect of her archaeology...the dig itself.

Lead her to the site...but allow her to uncover the artefacts herself.

As we work from a place of non knowing, with an open and inquiring mind, we are likely to notice previously concealed footprints. And when we are confronted with a multitude of possibilities, it would be wise to follow our client's lead. For that is the true path of exhilarating growth....both ours and hers.

Make no mistake about this, there are guidelines of

great value available to us, and there will come a time when even the most obscure framework becomes important to our work.

Knowledge of any system whatsoever is bankable. The caveat is that when you deal with an individual, **be sure and deal with her as an individual, exactly as she is, not as any particular body of knowledge says she is or should be.**

It's traditional to speak of the *integrity of a system,* which is a very pregnant phrase. It suggests that we must accept the entire system, exactly as presented, as a complete and indivisible unit.

The fantasy is that we must apply only that one system during the bodywork processing or else our results may be diluted. Mix competing brands together and they may cancel each other out, or worse. This is no more than an effort to force us to choose one system over its competitors when no choice is really necessary. With so many wonderful systems to play with, any choice becomes a deprivation.

And deprivation is not our natural condition. There is no rational need to work, or to live in scarcity, not when we can so easily surround ourselves with abundance. If you choose scarcity you inherit those notorious in-laws sophistry and dogma...as well as their first cousins effort and stress.

Choose abundance and you choose the sunshine. Knowledge blossoms and grows as it is shared. Bodywork is a unified whole, not meant to be applied in selected fragments. Systems need not be competitors guarding their supposed secrets from one another. When we work in abundance, we enrich each other...and our bodies rejoice.

If any two processes are not compatible in the same body at the same time, that body will be the first to realize it and it will definitely tell you all about it...loudly! If there is a complaint, if the body does object, it's likely the manner of application rather than the process itself that the body objects to.

Abundance prospers! The more we share our work, the more we demonstrate it to others, the better our work becomes.

As I alternate between the teacher/student/client labels the quality of each of them profits.

Choosing scarcity is just not logical to our work. My experience of truly outstanding bodyworkers throughout the world, is that very few of them hesitate to share their knowledge. Their very effectiveness appears to derive from their abundance.

There is an increasing tendency for the most successful bodyworkers to sooner or later transcend their systems. Bit by bit they incorporate a variety of elements into their work, borrowing from every system they encounter. These highly successful people become practical demonstrations that systems are never truly incompatible.

They have discovered a basic secret of bodywork. They know that each body we encounter is a complete universe with its own unique system of rules. Advanced bodyworkers understand and honor those rules, and tend to impose fewer of their own preferences onto their clients. They either transcend the boundaries of their system or they expand those boundaries.

Properly done, a session always expands, to some degree, the horizon of the practitioner as well as the client.

We learn body talk by removing our constraints and broadening our perspectives...by taking all outside input and incorporating it into our vocabulary...and most of all by listening with our whole body.

Our fluency grows as we consider the words of those outside our field. By listening to those who address our situation from an entirely different frame of reference, and by so doing they help us to consider even more possibilities, and because of them there are even fewer limitations on our work.

The longer we work within such a framework, the more all encompassing our work tends to become. With more of the pieces at our disposal, a blending of all the techniques occurs quite smoothly and naturally.

How does all this work in practice?

If a client, say a Cynthia, comes into my office, what does her processing look like? As a Chiropractor, do I look to her spine and adjust her...or do I rolf her? How do I decide if she's a candidate for Aston-Patterning, Cranial-Sacral Unwinding or Rosen Therapy? Which of the countless massage, reflexive, deep tissue, energy or Shamanistic techniques do I apply with Cynthia?

What do I actually do with this Cynthia?

The truth is, of course, that I do none of the above. I don't Rolf Cynthia. I don't adjust Cynthia. What I do is Cynthia. Simply Cynthia.

Every system at its very best is only an approximation of how to Cynthia. No single system can encompass a Cynthia. Each does have a piece, a very lovely and important piece to be sure, but it is not the package, and we need it all to complete a Cynthia.

The work itself must derive from Cynthia.

So the very best system of all...is to listen...and then Cynthia.

Here's Looking at You, Kid!

I was fortunate to grow up with Hollywood practically in my back yard. Fortunate because in Hollywood every working actor knows the necessity of looking into all the diverse elements of any given situation. The actor knows that an effective scene involves more than just reciting his lines, he knows that before his first words are spoken, all the elements central to his character, all the events leading up to this moment must be emotionally acknowledged.

The actor must know how to center himself, check his emotional state and ask himself some pertinent questions. What's going on in this scene? What's the event? What's the subtext beneath the words? What past behaviors are responsible for this situation we now find ourselves in? What do we wish to change about this situation?

The artistry lies in the preparation, in the creation of the "moment before." It's this preparation that creates the magic that makes a scene worth remembering.

It's the same with any form of healing. Our work doesn't start when we lay our hands on flesh. We too must have our "moment before." We too must resist the powerful temptation to hurry on in and change something, resist the insistent urge "to get it on."

Body Secrets

First we must *listen* to this body before us. So...clear your eyes as well as your ears, so you can understand what you are hearing. Approach with your heart as well as your eyes open and be aware that with your first words you have made a contact, and even before that with your first glance, and even before that with your first thoughts and attitudes.

The very looseness of your body transmits a message to the client. A message that is received and instantly understood on the tissue if not the intellectual level and from here on in it will influence your every interaction together.

Your energy patterns, extending far beyond your flesh, reach out and caress the energy fields of your client.

If the reality of this contact seems foreign to you, don't worry. It won't for long. You've only been hiding the experience from yourself.

Bodywork is about exploring and reclaiming such forgotten sensitivities as these. You will continually rediscover that working with your client is also working with yourself and that as your client expands, so will you.

To begin any exploration we need a map and a sense of direction. It is gratifying to know where we are, where we want to go, and have at least a vague idea of how to get there. This is basic to our "moment before."

Here's Looking at You, Kid

Our first coordinates come from the *attitude of the client toward his own body.* He may tend to speak of his body as it used to be, or as he hopes it will be sometime in the future, or as he thinks it should be. Keep his focus in present time.

"Right now. Today. This very second. What are your feelings about your body?"

Have him consider his body as a whole, as well as all the sub units (such as his arms)...and then their individual parts (such as his right little finger)...if it seems appropriate.

Have him talk of his most favored and his least favored areas. Listen carefully to his choice of words, and to his gestures, and to the quality of his voice as he talks of his body. Does his presentation match the content of his words?

This may be an uncomfortable introduction to the bodywork process for him. It is often threatening but it is always valuable. If he doesn't want to play, don't insist on it. It will all come out somewhere down the line, just at a more leisurely pace. It's more effective in the long run to allow him to ease into awareness at his own rate.

Looking into the mirror may also be a confrontation for him. If he is adverse to talking about his body it will probably be even more difficult for him to look at it. This too is part of our "moment before."

You might explain to your client that if what the two of you see in the mirror differs radically, what it does not mean is that one of you is wrong, you are just looking at a shared

91

reality from different perspectives.

Most of us have never really seen ourselves in a mirror. We may have looked, but probably actually never seen behind the cosmetics. Our client probably never spent time trying to penetrate his shadows, this may be a new experience for him. Our task is to help him experience without undue emotional overlay, without blurring or clouding around the edges.

Keep it light. maneuver him into an easy acceptance of what could be a challenging confrontation. Make sure he understands that nothing he sees is immutable, that everything we consider together is changeable.

Assure him also that this is not a test. There is no passing or failure here. **This is only an exploration into awareness,** an introduction to the parameters of his very pliable body, to the plasticity which affords us such a multitude of reference points. Our immediate goal at this point is to bring these reference points to the foreground of his consciousness.

If there seems to be a lot of emphasis on awareness it's because awareness appears to be the almost indispensable ingredient of conscious transformation.

To promote awareness I have full length mirrors available first for my client to reacquaint himself with his body, and later to monitor his changing landmarks.

First we consider his body in the static posture. Together we look for areas of compression, tissues compacted into spaces too small for comfortable living. As we find a compression we look to its relationships, alert for the slightest trace of structural incompatibilities.

It supports the process to emphasize whichever landmarks are most easily seen by the client. Later he can use these same landmarks to visually assess his progress from session to session and thereby more thoroughly own his results.

We are looking at a three dimensional body, but in the beginning it is helpful to isolate a single dimension and focus on *symmetry,* which will lead us to compression.

We can find and evaluate symmetry through comparisons of *vertical length.* The more points of vertical length we cover, the more our client understands the mutual influence that each of his body parts have on one another. Since these relationships will change so quickly once we begin working, they can be tools to help him understand his structural patterns and to modify his functional habits.

The odyssey begins by observing the client's body, first in stillness and then in motion. I like to start with what seems to the client as the most unchangeable aspect of all, and that which he most often overlooks.....his face.

Look to his eyes. Are they even? Is one of them closer to the ceiling than the other? Which one and by how much? Look to the ears. Which ear is closer to the ceiling? By how much?

Allow him to make the discoveries.

If the eyes and the ears are uneven, have him note if the higher eye and higher ear are on the same, or on opposite sides of his face. Note how each of these patterns affect the shape of his head. Help him to explore details of other facial asymmetries.

Decide with him which side of an asymmetrical structure seems the more appropriate to that structure, the vertically short or the vertically long side.

We are looking at **a series of relationships.** Bodywork starts and finishes with relationships of every variety, relationships between every conceivable part of our client's body, his relationship to each of them, and to himself, and to every aspect of his environment....as well as to his bodyworker. Each is a factor in our work. Each has its sphere of influence. As we alter any one of them the impact ripples throughout the system.

We can follow the tracts of compression to better understand the complexities of these reciprocal relationships. We have considered vertical length, we can now make further evaluations through comparisons of *horizontal length,* the width of the body from a central line.

Postulate a bisecting line and note which side extends out the furthest. Relate these findings to what you discovered about vertical length, and now the body before you has two dimensions.

Consider the *depth* of the body, that area from the front to the back. Does one side differ from another? How does it fit into the picture?

As your client faces the mirror help him to note which side of his chest, or his pelvis, or his hips, is closer to the mirror. Now we are dealing with rotational distortions and have shifted into viewing a three dimensional body.

Look for **rotational relationships.** If the thorax is rotated, is the pelvis also rotated? Consider all the elements of this relationship.

Do they rotate in the same direction? Do they rotate to the same degree? Are they a source of conflict and stress, or do they complement each other for the greater ease of the body? If pain is a consideration, how does it relate to this rotational intersection? Is it possible that here we are looking at two combatants using the lower back as their battleground? What are the client's feelings about this area of his body?

This gathering of information is an ongoing process, central to the continuing flow of bodywork. The more detailed his awareness, the faster his processing.

The very act of focusing awareness promotes a change and creates a climate encouraging even further and more profound changes.

Our client can more easily assimilate the changes if we continually focus his awareness on what is happening to him and how his physical holding patterns are connected to whatever emotions that may be rising within.

Our intention is to first ease him out of his compressions, and then educate him to use his newly reorganized body more efficiently.

It is transformation we are courting now and transformation prefers a partner with an easy manner. So be attentive to the needs of your client. He may crave, even require, a steady diet of reassurance about the plastic nature of his body.

Help him to understand that the elements you have chosen to observe are only individual aspects of a relationship. As any single variable of this relationship is changed, the relationship itself is changed. And if your client worries that his changes may not last, help him to examine his thoughts about the nature of change itself.

Consider with your client his *knees*. That intersection where the upper and the lower legs meet. Note the directionality of the tissue above and below the knee. Does it suggest compatibility, or is there another obvious struggle taking place here too with the knee joint catching it from both sides? Note the directionality of his knees themselves. Right? Left? Down? At what angle? How does one knee compare to the other? What are his feelings about his knees? Could he possibly be weak kneed?

To understand what your client stands on, as well as what he stands for, examine his base of support. Do his feet support his ankles? What are the structural components of his feet that might contribute to non-support? How do the feet differ?

Are the mechanics of his feet perfectly clear to you? Somewhat overcast? Totally obscured?

Be easy with yourself!
It all comes with awareness and it starts with the looking. For the present just scout the signs of compression and pose yourself a few gentle questions.

*Is there a visual tightness present? If there is, is

there also a visual looseness somewhere in the area? What might the relationship between them be?

*What is the purpose of the toes in this static posture? Do they lay straight and easily relaxed on the surface of the floor or have they seemingly been pressed into service to brace against the possibility of an earthquake?

*What does the heel contribute to this support pattern? Is there some part of this complex that appears as if it is not being put to appropriate use?

*Note the pattern of weight distribution throughout the foot. Then follow its trail up the body.

Look and contemplate as through the eyes of a carpenter because that is exactly what you are. If you had constructed this body, is this how you would have done it? If not, what would you like to change?

It's a game to be enjoyed, and it works infinitely better when you both take pleasure in the process. It's not a ritual and it wasn't meant to be solemn. Efficiency hangs with the light and the easy.

As you look at the front of the body in its entirety, note how one side may differ from the other. Are the differences between the right and left sides consistent throughout the body? What might the implications of this be? What does the right side signify? What about the left? What does the back signify? Then since the back is the alter ego of the front, consider the two of them at the same time.

Pay the same amount of attention to his side view as you did to the front. As it was with the front so it is with the side. (I find it helpful to have my workroom mirrored in a manner in which the client can see his front and both his sides at the same time.)

Note how one side differs from the other. As seen from this angle are right side and left side differences consistent throughout the body?

You can start the investigation from anywhere that grabs your eye. Or you might begin by contemplating the ankle/heel complex.

Contemplate how this relationship of the ankle to the heel might possibly affect the rest of the foot, as well as the knee, and of course the hip, and any other place up above that has caught your interest. Consider the influence of the heel on any problem areas you may have noticed.

Is there too little or too much heel and how might this relate to his personality? Where does he stand on the continuum from "round heels" to "push over" to "stubborn ass?" ...As you change the heel do you imagine the personality might also change?

Examine the client's vertical alignment as a whole, noticing particularly where this verticality wanders away from a central line, or appears to be missing altogether. As with horizontal alignment, consider verticality from the standpoint of *compression* and *distortion* and *discomfort.*

Allow your body as well as your eyes to listen to the tone of these tissues. Do you sense a cry for help? Do some tissues seem to stand out as distinct from their neighbors? Can you recognize those tissues that are hiding behind a facade of rigidity and masquerading as bone? In the absence of balance a body sorely needs such strategies as this.

We are looking at a complex structure with unlimited components and any component may be more easily understood by examining its relationships.

Do not allow yourself to become discouraged or frustrated. This is an exploration. It's a game, so treat it as such. Accept this attitude for it encourages continual learning.

So be aware that when you feel a twinge of frustration, it's only because you are learning something you didn't know before. Remind yourself that this is a new experience, a personal and professional growth process. You are only uncomfortable because of this newness. If you already knew the process you would feel neither frustrated nor awkward....and you wouldn't be learning anything new either. Take a nice deep breath and let the game continue.

As you notice any compression, notice its relationships...how the rest of the body conspires to keep it intact. You may eventually notice that no part can exist in isolation.

It's useful to view the body as a complex mass of compensations, as a bodywide support system for each original compression. All intertwined. Move one tissue and you set off a chain of events that undulates throughout the web.

Compensatory areas themselves tend to become

more rigid than their neighbors. Their tissues become confused about their primary job. They escalate into secondary areas of stress that themselves clamor for attention.

They have joined the category of **Confused Tissue** which has a certain feel about it that you will come to recognize with experience.

When we do reach in and lift out some long overlooked insult to the body, the transformation goes smoother and lasts longer if we also address ourself throughout its entire support system.

But for now, we are still gathering information, so consider the feet in their entirety, noting how their distribution of body weight heavily influences all the structural relationships above.

How does the head reflect this distribution, and how do the feet in turn, reflect and maintain the position of the head?

The more you seek out such relationships, the more they will call to you, and the more apparent the logic of the system will become.

Some artists of the body have become so adept that they can accurately predict the whole after viewing only a small part, extrapolating from one part to another, moving with dexterity from the very general to the extremely specific and back again.

I was privileged to witness a most dramatic demonstration of this ability during a class with Ida Rolf at Big

Sur, California. Her demonstration model, who was previously unknown to her, arrived that chilly morning wearing a heavy overcoat. She had her first look at him as he entered the doorway, and immediately awed me with her initial remarks to the class: "I trust everyone sees that his fifth lumbar vertebra is rotated."

Of course it was! It wouldn't dare have been anything other as all who knew Ida will surely attest.

I thought at first that this was magic. Then I concluded that Ida Rolf was simply more attuned to body messages than the rest of us. Now I realize that my initial reactions were absolutely correct. It was magic! She was functioning at a peak of awareness which may quite likely be the best kind of magic there is, the possible kind, the kind available to us all.

If you are not yet on such a plateau, you can for the present understand that such a level of awareness **is** available to you. It is to be found within the looking, and the listening with all of your senses.

Mirrors are a master teacher. Watch yourself in motion. Watch your client in motion. As an aid to developing your visual acuity enlist verbal feedback from your client as he watches himself in the mirror.

Remember always that we wear the hat of a teacher. So be a good teacher and allow the client to truly discover for himself, to recognize and to understand his own restrictions.

Your job is to guide him toward these discoveries, not make them for him. His job is the searching and the uncovering, both of lasting importance.

Don't cheat him of the experience. Use all your tools to encourage the development of all his powers.

Some bodyworkers use video tape to educate their clients. Others take a series of Polaroid pictures immediately before and after each session. Pictures of his front, his back, and of each side. Both methods are of proven value.

I prefer mirrors because they offer a more immediate form of feedback. The client is able to associate what he sees happening in the mirror with an immediate body sensation.

Share with your client just what you are looking for and what you are noticing as he moves around the room. This will focus his attention and encourage his feedback.

Shift your awareness once again. Just prior to actually moving his body, the client will make preparations to move. Look to the mechanics of his preparations. Where does the movement actually start in his body? What part of his body initiates the movement?

Don't let your expectations limit your observations.

As he moves....What do you notice moving first? What do you notice moving the least? Do you notice what would seem to be an excess of movement anywhere?

What mood do you sense underlying his movements? Do the parts harmonize? Is the rhythm of the tissue in sync with its neighbors? Are his movements accompanied by a symphony, or just a noise?

Focus special attention on **movements** of his hip and pelvic area. Register the amount of movement and be fairly precise about it. We can use this measurement as a standard of improvement. Although it may be appropriate to first note if his pelvis moves at all.

Once you've noted the *quantity,* then consider the *quality* of the movement. Does it promenade proudly throughout the pelvis or does it carefully skip all around it? What factors seem to be restricting free pelvic movement?

Restrictions in the pelvis, or anywhere else for that matter, may originate absolutely anywhere, including the mind. **Particularly in the mind!** What are the attitudes and comments of society about this pelvic movement? It may be helpful to try on the pattern for size, mock it up with your own body, and notice whatever thoughts or emotions that may arise as you move within its confines.

Help your client explore exactly how he feels when allowing his hips to swing freely.

What does it suggest to him?

What does it suggest to you?

Women clients often think of a "loose woman."

Male clients have different concerns: "I can't walk like that. People will think I'm gay."

Or: "I can't walk like that. People will know I'm gay."

Whatever the rationale, there is just too much effort, too much stress, holding too many hips, too damn rigid. There is no valid reason to deny this soul the ease and the grace that originally comes with the territory.

Movements are meant to fluidly ripple throughout the body. Hip swinging is a natural and efficient action, seen among all cultures of the world, noticeable particularly in male and female world class athletes, in dancers, in all graceful peoples...unless of course it's been suppressed.

It's a natural movement that takes active effort to keep in check. An effort which carries an expensive price-tag. Find a chronic back problem and you usually find a rigid pelvic and hip combination walking the same trail. This is a repressive mechanism that creates an increasingly rigid physical structure with behaviors and attitudes that match.

The cost of structural misuse is always diminished movement.

So if the knees are locked and can no longer function as shock absorbers, what effect might this have on the hips?

What if the feet forget their own function as shock absorbers, and wander off on strange trajectories of their own, how would this dampen appropriate body movement? Note particularly how it might affect the pelvis.

Look also to the walking *stride*. Is it appropriate for this body it propels? Might it be too short or too long for this structure? Might it possibly be too wide or too narrow? Might it even be just right? Notice how each of these affects pelvic movement.

Every movement difficulty has the same answer...**balance**. Which is both the hero of the story and the ultimate in simplicity. Balanced movement is nothing more than movement appropriate to the structure it moves.

We can better understand our client's balance as we sense our own. So stand yourself up before a full length mirror and watch the reflection as you try on each of the above variations. Notice the effect of each of them on your movement patterns. As you play with them, look for the possibility of subtle shifts in your emotional processes.

In the beginning it is usually easier to see than to feel your own rigidities. They are the unnoticed constant, blending with overlooked familiarity into background.

Whatever is the most familiar to us is what we seem to subconsciously understand to be the norm. It doesn't matter how aberrated that norm may appear to others. Which has very profound implications for our work, a significance factor we can not afford to ignore. What we need now is an even higher degree of awareness...of ourselves and of our clients.

Focus your client's attention on his rigidities and help him move the familiar and unnoticed compressions into the foreground of his consciousness.

He may be aware of his rigidities but mistake them for his strengths.

The most common example is *the hyperextended knee syndrome,* which has assumed plague-like proportions in our society. A knee rigidity that is so familiar, so much a part of the everyday background, that once it is released clients report an initial experience of weakness and lack of support.

It helps maximize the process if we maintain a continual exploration into our client's perceptions, and guide him to contrast the feel of an efficient muscle with a rigid muscle. Help him to physically understand how his locked knees affect the rest of the body, to experience his knees as traffic policemen directing stress to other areas of the body.

Cheer on his explorations.

And his dance of transformation will begin to quicken as he senses the relationships between his parts, and *physically* comes to understand the value of flexibility and ease of movement.

Then, as his physical changes become increasingly integrated into his everyday experience, he will learn to relate his emotional behaviors to their structural and functional foundations.

It's all in the awareness, which all starts with the looking.

So........**Here's looking at you, kid!**

It's All So.........Touching

A kiss is just a kiss, a sigh is just a sigh, but the touch of a bodyworker....ahhh, now that's something else.

It's a touch that's so much more than a touch. It's a touch to arouse memories and awaken feelings that have been slumbering just below the covers of consciousness.

It's a laying on of hands. An intimate conversation with the soul.

This is what it can be. This is what it should be. This is what it all too often is not. The secrets of the touch are in the mechanics. Virtuosity is only a matter of awareness.

...but it's never innocent!

Place a hand upon a body and, in that very instant, that body is also placed upon your hand, each simultaneously transmitting and receiving in a continuous process of shaping and reshaping and responding to each other's input. It's that most intricate of social interactions; a completely candid and intimate discourse.

You may have noticed that it's easier to carry on a conversation when neither of you is shouting. It's the same with touch, the easiest touch picks up the softest whispers. To miss as little as possible, keep your hand *light and easy,* and touch with intention. Let your hands linger awhile, making small talk, encouraging mutual ease in both your tissues.

This is the singular touch of an understanding hand. Which considering its scarcity must surely be more complex than it appears. This innocent looking touch can at one moment comfort your soul, and the next rock your senses with a glimpse into the infinite. It can bring out the best or the worst in us. It seems to understand our tissues so very well, and yet is so very poorly understood itself.

There is even a viewpoint currently in vogue among the healing arts that divides touch into information gathering and therapeutic functions. It's completely artificial of course, no more than a convenient fiction, possibly helpful for teaching purposes.

Palpation is "to examine by touching." But there is no such thing as pure examination, no such thing as using your hands to gather uncontaminated information. It's impossible to touch a body without altering it in some way to some degree.

The slightest touch can leave lingering footprints, or the merest suggestion of ever having been present, but each does leave its mark. Which taken together with all the other miscellaneous physical contacts sums up to the feelings and understandings this body has about its world.

We tend to overlook such casual input, to ignore its existence in the equation, but as a bodyworker's eye develops the prints will ever more boldly step out and reveal themselves.

Before we add our own input to this body before us, we would do well to witness and appreciate it as it is at this moment. To behold it without preconceptions, without biased overlay, letting whatever there is present splash gently over our consciousness before we touch it and change it. Look at this body as if you are looking at a body for the very first time. Defer your evaluations until later. For now just let your senses record energy patterns.

You will come to see that the touch connection is never so innocent as you might have once suspected. The body doesn't forget. Your very first contacts with your client are variables that will give direction to your work, that will shape the quality of your relationship and influence the range of possibilities you can explore together.

On the mechanics of the touch connection.

Look for flesh to flesh compatibility. The angle and speed of your approaching hand influences tissue rapport. We want neither to appear hesitant nor to frighten the tissues. Our hands must communicate confidence and safety.

After you have made contact and the tissues are relaxed, keep your hand soft, and slowly allow your body weight to transmit down your arms, through your fingers and your palms and into the tissues.

Not force, not strength, not effort, just the weight of your shifting body. Move your entire body, allowing gravity itself to ease the pressure onto the layer of your choice.

Stay conscious of the shape you give to both the speed and the direction of your working weight.

It's easily as important how you release the pressure as how you apply it. Possibly even more so. Once you have earned the trust of these tissues, they may lower their guard and invite you in for a visit. For them it's a time of extreme vulnerability. If you jump and run, you can send them into a state of shock, leaving them feeling disoriented and abandoned and they will not be so quick to relax their defenses the next time around.

Your initial purpose may be to collect information, but **the very shape of your hand imparts a suggestion,** and tissues are notoriously suggestible, as well as being extremely sensitive to all the nuances.

Fundamentally, this is a continuation of our visual inspection, with the added element of touch. **Mold your hand to the contours of the flesh,** being careful not to flatten the area or shape it to match your hand. Rather, shape your hand to match the area.

To examine by touching...slowly, gently, palpate for areas with less resiliency than their neighbors. Let your hands search out tissue that tells you it is holding fast and rigid and can't let go. Let all your senses experience the full range of the energy residing in these tissues, mentally cataloging differences in both their level and their character. Map those areas with diminished or unusual energy patterns for further investigation.

Palpate with the client both standing and lying down. You can pick up additional information by repeating the same procedures in new positions.

Do the targeted areas retain the same qualities lying down as they did when the client was on her feet?

Consider how this shift in gravity affects her rigidities and compressions. If an area remains the same in both positions, in the horizontal and the vertical, then that area is predominantly a structural situation. The lesions are physically locked into the tissues, and to release them physical manipulation becomes the procedure of choice.

If the nature of the patterns changes with the change in position, they are basically of a functional character. It's their **method of use** that creates and maintains the compressions. So here movement education becomes the preferred procedure.

The process is an ongoing exploration into the living mechanics of a specific structure unique to this specific client.

Our work deals with the biomechanics of the individual, always of the individual. Her biomechanics are never an abstraction existing outside of her structure. In our client's daily course of events her singular structure is continually in the process of reshaping her mechanics. Every remolding of her physical body that we initiate will also be reflected by a corresponding shift in her movements.

Following a unit of bodywork we must explore with our client how she can best adapt her new movements to a somewhat unfamiliar structure. It's up to her to actively claim her new parameters. We can only guide and suggest. It's another exercise in sensitivity, sensitivity to all the new possibilities, and the exercise itself functions as a servo-mechanism to even further modify her structure.

We can't make the mistake of assuming that, once she is capable of moving with more ease, she will automatically do so to the full extent possible. Her structure will never quite be the same, never as restricted as it once was, but this using of all the freedoms that are now available to her is another issue. Freedoms are not that easy to claim or to hold. Her outdated visual cues continue to reinforce ancient restrictions that have left ghostly fingerprints on her psyche. Habit alone may keep her corralled within ethereal fences.

Physical expressions of restriction prefer to dwell in the relative anonymity of the fascial system. Keep in mind the impossibility of any abstraction accurately or completely representing the truth of a situation and then reflect upon the following, a functional abstraction of the fascial system that can take us home...

We have this fascial body that consists of layer upon multiple layer of connective tissue, which runs continuously throughout the body from head to toe. Each muscle and each internal organ wraps itself within these layers.

In its natural state, in the absence of compressive restrictions, fascial planes will glide smoothly and unhindered over other fascial planes. Healthy fascia displays a certain internal mobility which may be decreased or lost altogether following any traumatic insult to the body.

The insult may impact on any of our bodies, the emotional, the spiritual, or the intellectual body, but its ultimate expression is in the fascial body.

We may view our work quite accurately as that of restoring lost mobility to these fascial highways. We are the road crew, and this is our highway.

This is a multilayered system in a three dimensional body, so we must be aware of the depth we wish to engage. It's always a matter of objectives. How *deep* and how *extensive* is the restriction?

We may choose to work with a broad section of the body, with many layers, or with a single specific layer, but we must work with awareness and intention. With a little attention and a little practice the layers will make themselves known. That's a guarantee. Palpate with intent and awareness, which is another way of saying with adroitness and finesse, and the layers will reveal themselves.

Palpation is an art and a skill, and like all skills it improves with practice. Awareness is the key ingredient of efficient practice. Just keep focused on what is under your hand.

It's essential that you practice without judging your progress or your skills. You can do all that later. What works best for now is to maintain an internal atmosphere that contributes to your relaxation. **Enjoy** the learning process and **celebrate** all your discoveries.

As soon as a trace of frustration arises drop it. Remind yourself of what this is really all about. You are only frustrated because you are moving into areas previously unknown to you. You are learning new skills and are only showing impatience with yourself.

Take another deep breath...exhale....and continue.... Your contact skills are in a continual state of refinement when you practice within this perspective. It's simply a matter of nourishing yourself. Of being as easy with yourself as you would be with someone you love. Efficiency and ease have this thing going on between them. They're really quite an item.

During this cultivation and harvesting of your innate listening skills you may hear murmurs of strange and curious happenings. Of events transcending both your experience and your imagination. Whatever the content, don't deny your experience. Don't write it off as fantasy. Listen for what is there to be told, not what you expect to be there or have been led to believe would be there, listen to what is actually there. The possibilities are greater than all of our expectations. If we can imagine it, it may be there. Even if we can't imagine it, it may still be there.

The secret to good listening is to place no limitations on yourself and accept no limitations placed by others. Your results depend on it. Listen to your body, listen to your client's body, listen to the Universe and then let your results be your guide.

Along this fascial highway you may encounter a variety of holding patterns, detours that skirt areas long ago abandoned as impassable. Let each of them become your teacher. Introduce yourself and make polite conversation. Admire its **shape.** Each will have a definite functional shape about it. All you can predict about this shape for sure is that it won't be straight. The body doesn't seem to care for this concept of straight.

The body prefers the spiral as its working configuration. **The spiral**: an all purpose three dimensional wave that has quite incredible properties. The spiral can connect all the diverse areas of the body, as well as reconcile polarities. Incompatibilities can connect and resolve their differences under the auspices of the spiral. Energy is trapped in spirals. Compressions are maintained and released in spirals. There is no situation that can not be more easily approached through the spiral. It's the basic weave in the fabric of body language.

Honor the qualities of each individual spiral. Conform to its vastness, and its depth, and its shape, and of course its speed. Notice how it may abruptly change directions on you.

It's tricky and devious! Don't let it lose you.

Actually it's neither tricky nor devious, it just likes to pretend that it is.

It appreciates us the most when we impose as little of ourselves as possible. If we try to palm off a bit too much, the spiral will just fade off into the sunset and lie low for a while.

The way to help tissues release their compressions is to escort them home and quietly call their attention to alternative pathways. **Follow** them in the direction they have already chosen and, when you reach a barrier, settle down as comfortably as possible and wait a while. Often it's enough to just make camp, at other times you may need to add your energy to that which is already present.

This body itself will lead you through the barriers. And please remember not to walk on the grass. Retrace your steps. Tissues appreciate it when we leave on the same path on which we entered.

At some point it will become apparent to you just how exceptionally easy it is to change a body. It may also cross your mind that it would be more direct to forget all this nonsense and simply reposition tissue to suit your own tastes. When the body does not move as quickly as we would like, the temptation may be to override it...for its own good of course...to impose what we know to be best for it.

That could be a mistake. It's because of this that a great many seasoned bodyworkers oppose indiscriminate training of new practitioners. They already spend too much of their time and effort correcting mistakes imposed by others.

It is easy to change the structure. Maybe too easy! Changes can come easily and quickly, but the *integration* of these changes into the structure, now that's another story altogether. Changes must *blend* into their environment. There are no short cuts here. Move too quickly and the system rebels once more.

Moving tissue around without regard for why it is there in the first place can create some very unsubtle side effects. Try coercing the body and it will surrender a superficial area of tension but hold on to the basic pattern at an even more profound level. We have strengthened the very position we wanted to remove. We have added even further resistance to a defensive pattern already well entrenched. The pattern may have been altered, but it has certainly not been eliminated.

More on the elements of touch......

The **contours** of the flesh are not random. Don't ignore them. They are not there without reason. They represent the current preferences of the body. Match the contours of your hand to those of the body and the tissues will sense your understanding and sigh with relief. You have made a friend.

Listen to the *tone* of the tissue. Mold your hand softly around a tonal area and just sit quietly. The tissue also has a *grain,* acknowledge this too in your explorations.

The body appreciates well mannered and gallant visitors. The key to good manners is to first be gentle with yourself, then you can be gentle with the tissues, and they will become more confident and less likely to scare and freeze up on you.

Each area of compression has its own personality, its own emotional motif with almost imperceptible dimensions that range throughout the entire emotional spectrum. Compressions may encompass fear, embarrassment, apprehension, anger, guilt, or elements of them all at the same time.

When you think you imagine an emotion arising from a given area of the body, the odds are very good that your imaginings are quite accurate. You have probably contacted that very emotion. You may have just roused it from its resting spot. Receive the communication and acknowledge it. The body under your hands will understand and find you trustworthy, and reward you with even more of its confidences.

How open are you to such communications?

Because that's how many will be offered to you. So put your doubts aside. Trust your hands and your bodily senses. Trust yourself. This too will be transmitted through your touch.

The tissue is named integrity. It yearns for freedom even while under the shadow of an apprehensive ego. Show the body safety, and give it the slightest chance to unwrap itself and it runs to show you the way. Then it's only a matter of following. Once you speak the language, it's as easy as that.

One for the money.....

Every place you position your hands has an inherent *directionality* to it. It's the path of easiest movement. To find it, place your hand lightly and relaxed on a selected area and test the tissue tension in each direction. One path will show itself as clearly more appropriate than the others. You might encourage your client to add her perceptions to the process.

This path of movement will be angular but hardly predictable. It may remain in one plane or wind from layer to layer. It may move in a beautiful classical arc only to sharply and suddenly reverse upon itself, or it might even follow a completely erratic course. But whatever the course, it leads to an eventual release. Notice how the path takes you as much as where it takes you.

Each path has its own *speed.* Try to match it. Move too fast and you scare it and from deep within it tightens itself up. Frightened tissue doesn't like to talk all that much. Particularly if you are the one who frightened it in the first place.

Slowly...very slowly...with the proper amount of restraint you may be able to persuade a reluctant tissue to walk a little ways with you. Tissues respond to sweet talk more than force. Court them. If you can't match their speed, at least be inclined to the slow and the gentle. This is your testimony of good will. The nice body before you understands your intentions and may be quite touched by them.

It's in the hands. It's through your hands that you get the information that creates the magic. You touch...and they feel...and together you invoke the spirits of freedom.

So.......**once more with feeling!**

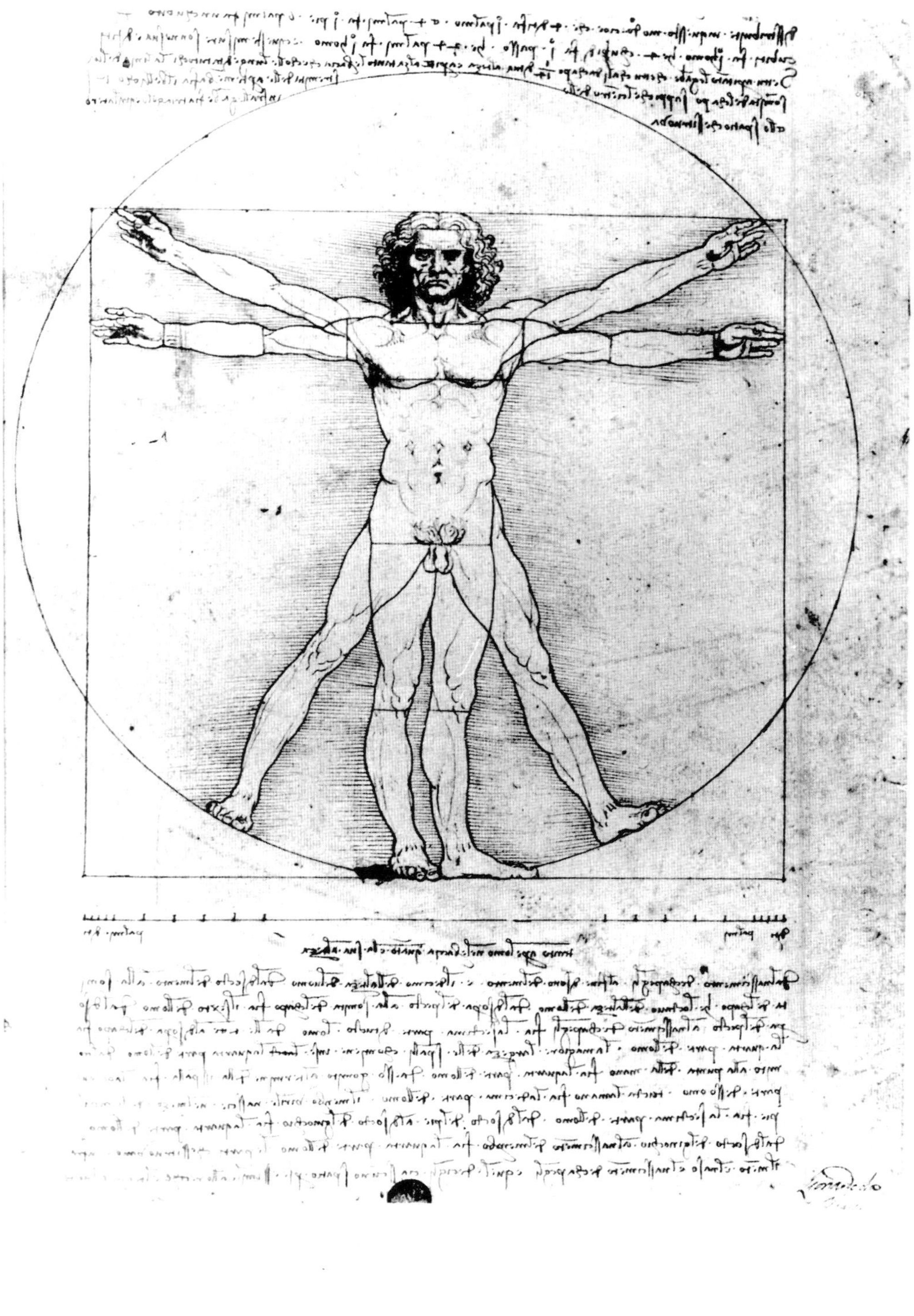

Hot Hands on the Old Kazoo

So to get on with it...it's a matter of **problem solving**....deciding on a **specific event** that you would like to see evolve during this session and reflecting on how it might be enticed out of hiding.

Then selecting a **specific area** that seems somehow related to the event. You might choose to focus on a compressed rib cage that limits breathing capacity, with a specific goal to remind the rib cage of its true purpose, and to nudge it along the road towards meeting its potential, in other words, to release the ribs one from the other and encourage an easier exchange of oxygen. A specific focus yes, but the benefits of which will radiate throughout the system as a whole with far reaching effects.

Once you have identified the central problem, the next question is how to approach it. You have settled on an area of interest so now you need **a plan.** There are any number of effective ways to introduce yourself to a compression complex.

You might begin your voyage, it's a voyage in every sense of the word, by addressing the support system that surrounds the compression. You might venture to an adjacent area and prepare it for the impending release of its neighbor. You might choose to move to other nearby areas of secondary tension and ease them up a bit. Or, without any preliminaries at all, you could forge directly to the point of maximum discomfort and compression. (Occasionally they are the same.) You can address any situation directly or indirectly, head on or round about from anywhere throughout its underlying support system.

The choices are endless. If you are comfortable within a system, start as that system dictates and see if that is relevant to the problem. If you feel yourself drawn to a particular area, begin there. There is no place on the body that is legitimately inappropriate to your work. Some areas are just more immediately appropriate than others.

You can't go wrong so long as you follow the body's wishes and stay ever ready to surrender your original plan at a moment's notice. Drop it completely! It's not a question of being right or wrong, it has nothing to do with making correct choices, it is simply a matter of working in the moment and adjusting to a constantly changing situation.

Your next consideration is the positioning of your client. You position to meet a need. There is more involved than just laying the client down on the table.

One purpose is to create maximum comfort for yourself as well as your client. A position that is stressful to either of you can sabotage your best efforts. An appropriate position serves to expose the proper tissue layer to easy accessibility.

"On your back please." It's traditional in practice to have a client lie down without ever considering the nuances of position.

The possibilities are so much greater than "On your back please." You can position your client in any manner whatsoever: sitting, standing, laying on his back, on his front, on either side, or any combination or permutation of the above. The important factor is that you match the position both to your goal and to the situation in which you find yourself.

Pillows and towels of various sizes and densities are helpful accessories. They can ease the client's body and make your work more efficient. If they are used properly they can. If not, well......

You may have chosen to initially place the client in the supine position (face up) to work on his chest in order to free his diaphragm.

That is a basic, a beginning, now you must consider the effect of this position on the distribution of stress throughout his structure.

What is the relationship of his head to his neck, and of his neck to his chest?

Would his head like some additional height to support it?

How much?

Where?

The equation differs with each client. Too much under the head and you create compression in the throat. Too little, and the weight of the head falls back and you create a different compression. Experiment with a towel under his head, fold it to create maximum ease and balance. Good positioning is actually nothing more than finding this point.

Survey his entire body for areas of stress. Does his energy move freely throughout his structure? Gently push on the bottom of his feet, one at a time, then together. Note how the ripples move through the body and where they go off track.

This position, with the client on his back, might create a strain at the back of his knees, which can be released by positioning his heels just over the edge of the table, or by placing a towel or small pillow under his knees.

Notice how each of these solutions affect the small of the back in a slightly different manner. Notice too how each version has a differing affect on the quality of a movement travelling throughout his body.

There is a trap inherent in the use of pillows. We may unintentionally create slack in places where it is not of our choosing. We may wish to address the abdominal area and then so position our client that we completely miss the most superficial layers, and go directly to the deepest of abdominal musculature. If the superficial layers are already loosened it won't be a problem. But what if they aren't, what if they are tight and unyielding? If loosening this underlying structure prematurely doesn't compound old problems it will certainly create new ones.

If we consciously want to work on the deepest areas that's fine, we can do exactly that by placing one large support system to elevate his head-neck-and-upper-back complex, with a corresponding support system to raise his knees. We can alter the specifics with this position and effectively reach the very deepest of musculature within the abdominal cavity, even to the spine itself if that is our intent, and if the body has been prepared beforehand.

This bodywork process has been compared to peeling an onion. It is said that, like the onion, the body responds best when we open the most superficial layers first, and work from the outside in. But once again, there is no need to worry so long as we use all our senses and stay awake. The message, as always, is to keep our awareness functioning. The body itself will see us through any potential difficulties.

It illuminates your work to consider it in a variety of **conceptual frameworks**. There are so many ways to understand this body, so many abstractions, so many unique perspectives, and each of them may prove useful to us at some time or another. Rather than searching for apparent inconsistencies among the viewpoints, it's more efficient to recognize that we can gain new understandings from each of them. Be open to seeing the body from every possible angle.

The following is one such way to view the body, certainly not the major way, but a decidedly useful way.

Consider this body as if it were composed of a core and a sleeve with the core representing the central portion, all the deeper structures. And the sleeve, like it sounds, consisting of the outer coverings of the body, the more superficial layers.

Each with its own individual characteristics, the most obvious of which may be its location on the looseness/tightness continuum. Each seems to settle independently wherever it chooses on this continuum with little regard for the preferences of its alter-ego.

At one extreme is the loose sleeve, or superficial muscular hypotonicity if you like, and it feels like it sounds, flaccid. On the other end of the spectrum is deep muscular hypertonicity which feels like a rigid, unyielding, unresponding, center of iron.

The existence of both ends of the spectrum within a single body may seem a bit excessive, slightly incompatible, but they do often hang out together, and upon occasion will present distinctly conflicting messages to a somewhat confused outside world.

It's natural to speculate that the core represents the client as he actually is, while the sleeve expresses a survival mechanism, a cosmetic accommodation to an environment perceived as hostile. The sleeve may be the more obvious presentation, but the core is not all that well hidden from the world, or even from the consciousness of the client himself.

Our hands illuminate his paradoxes, and some part of his psyche nods in acknowledgement, remembering once again the existence of this shadowy domain.

The client is most often relieved when we penetrate this camouflage of the sleeve early on in a session. It builds his confidence in us, and as he senses our respect for his adaptations, he is inclined to share even his more profound secrets with us.

There are several forms to this dance of the core and the sleeve. The sleeve may faithfully mirror the core. There is a certain harmony in such a twinship, in the togetherness of a loose sleeve with a loose core, just as there is in the relationship of a tight sleeve with a tight core.

But when a tight sleeve waltzes with a loose core it's a different message altogether, one that will heavily influence the course of your sessions together. As your client progressively and consciously contrasts his inner and outer aspects, the reshaping of the dance quickens.

Prepare yourself for a completely different dance when a hard core steps out with a soft sleeve. There is a frequently volatile relationship between these two.

The work exposes us to a continual flood of information. The body constantly keeps us up to date. Even as we palpate, we influence the tissues which in turn influences our touch which becomes increasingly therapeutic as we alter it to match incoming information.

Our plan is to ride the horse in the direction it's going. (Thank you, Werner)

At any stage of the processing it's always a matter of awareness. Listen to the music of the body and it will take you home.

We must sever any attachment we have to our original plan of action for this session. As brilliantly conceived as it undoubtedly was, it was never more than a guide, a place to start. The very best plan optimally remains in a state of continual re-evaluation throughout the session. At the slightest whisper drop it. The event of major importance is for us to humor the tissues. Allow them to have their little joke.

So how are we doing?...Your hands have talked with the tissues, you have met the compression of your choice, now stand your client up and see what the two of you have accomplished.

The changes, which may have been very apparent while he was laying down, will look somewhat different when he is on his feet. Note how these changes react to gravity and how his movements reflect these alterations.

Solicit feedback from the client as you and he check the guideposts. How does he experience the results? Does he tend to see results visually or is he more into feeling them? This is a good opportunity to educate his eyes, as well as his other senses, all his other senses. Scan with him again those selected reference points. But for sure don't limit his inspection to just those areas you have worked on. The most dramatic result may be in seemingly unrelated areas of compensation.

On a first visit I usually find it useful to get my client on his feet in a matter of five or ten minutes. His psychological, emotional, and tissue responses inform me of how he is likely to react to quick and easy physical changes, and as a side effect will demonstrate the effectiveness of this work to him, which in turn will increase the effectiveness of the work for him. There is a wealth of information to be gleaned from his attitudes that reflect a prognosis potential as well as the speed of tissue transformation.

Once you have engaged and released a specific area of compression you have to secure your gains. When this compression is released, **as much as it chooses to release at this time,** this is a complete **unit of work.** You must now help the body secure the benefits from this unit.

Following a compression release the area will look and move quite differently. The question becomes: **how can we help the system adapt to its new potential?**

Every compression is responsible for the creation of a compensatory muscular support system. The job now is to help the body physically dismantle the entire system. The body knows how, just listen and allow it to point your eyes, and then your hands toward those places most likely to cheer on and support the revitalization of the structure.

It's a matter of **integration** and **balance.** Let your hands search out and release areas of tension around the major joints. A friendly touch helps the ankles and the knees accommodate to the altered pattern of weight transference from above.

Once there was a bone considered sacred to a people, and they called it the sacrum. Some even thought the soul might make its home directly in front of this sacred area, and maybe it does, the location sounds about right. It's central to so many bodily processes, and it's definitely pivotal to all body processing.

When we touch the sacrum with care our influence will radiate throughout the system. This is not a major bone of contention but of integration.

Rest the weight of this sacred bone in the soft palm of your hand and ever so slowly *ease* the base footward into a most gentle stretch that allows all the vertebrae to breathe themselves into a natural realignment.

There's a bone at the other end of the spine that would also like a little attention. Let the palms of your hands cradle the occiput while your fingers gently loosen and lengthen the back of the neck and the entire back of the body. This is all essential to the integration and balancing of the structure.

Balance refers equally to **movement** which is the other side of integrating this unit of work into the system. It's a matter of education. The client's movement patterns are now in a state of transition. We can direct his awareness to the details of this negotiating process between his form and his movements. Homework assignments help him to more consciously participate in the negotiations that will continue long after he leaves your office.

Optimally, he should exit in as balanced and aware a state as possible. Each session should stand as a unit of work complete within itself. A compression has been released, and the results integrated into his system for integration into his life.

You validate his passport as the client leaves your office more visually graceful than when he came in, and when he is aware of his new opportunities and has a functional sense of how to use them.

...on with the dance!

Dance with the Guru

Oh oh, this is not a Cynthia on my table now. This is a delicate flower of a Linda, delicate and different. What do I do now? I certainly don't want to Cynthia her, that wouldn't be at all nice.

I can Cynthia, but can I Linda?

To blossom, all any flower really needs is a little appreciation and understanding. This one just waits for some encouragement to get her started. She may be a little bashful about talking with strangers, and I must seem a little strange to her at that.

A slow Tango to start might be just the ticket.

But I feel a tingling, I sense something a little out of the ordinary here...what if she is one of those strange ones I have heard about, those who would rather be right than happy? What if she is even willing to die to prove that she is right, and that she has always been right? What if she is one of those who has her positions, and mistakes herself for those positions and is willing to go down cemented to her positions rather than give them up? Then what shall I do?

The saving grace is that this lovely little Linda wouldn't even be here in the first place if something deep inside of her really didn't want to be. What I may be picking up are stray emanations from a very frightened ego that knows it's standing at the brink.

Well, that's the ego for you, but fortunately the body itself is quite another matter. It's not afraid to take the risk of intimacy. It welcomes an understanding suitor. It likes all the little attentions. Better than that, it supplies us with an endless army of teachers and interpreters to assist this courting process.

Countless body spirits are accessible to us if we but listen for them. An army of assorted devas stand ready to guide us through the more tricky passages. It's written into their job specifications. The motto of their service is: Let the Guru be your guide.

Some of these guides have their own large followings among different segments of the bodywork community. There are systems today that have come to specialize in listening to one particular melody and their practitioners become unusually adept at understanding the nuances of that particular dance.

It's a valuable experience for us all to spend time with such a group. Personally profitable as well as professionally exciting. Linger awhile, but beware of committing your eyes exclusively to their Guru. To expand your work hang out with all the guides that you can. Your work more fully flourishes in an atmosphere of abundance.

Dance with the Guru

The body speaks in many tongues, and one of them may have a special affinity just for you, may whisper secrets that only you can understand. But even if you are blessed with such a special guide, this does not excuse you from listening when other knowledgeable voices speak.

One reliable guide goes under the name of **fascial drag**. It tells wonderous tales of wild mobilities and reckless restrictions gallivanting throughout the fascial highway system. The most silent compression, hiding anywhere within the inner city or the outskirts of the body, will make its presence known through the auspices of this fascial network, and fascial drag is its spokesperson.

I even know some very clever medical practitioners who consult this voice as their primary tool of diagnosis. Imagine!

As bodyworkers we too lay claim to the same information. Our interest lies more in locating problem areas than in categories of illness, and this same fascial drag will lead us directly to the site of a compression.

If you have not experienced working with fascia, the following exercise will give you a tactile sense of the process.

Cover a table with a bed sheet and place a coin in the middle. With both hands on an end of the sheet, slowly and gently take out the slack and experience the restriction caused by the coin.

Have a friend place the coin for you while your eyes are closed, and then try to locate it. This is the same principle that Chiropractors use when they place a hair in a book and trace its outline through a page. First through one page, then another and another. Nothing substitutes for actual palpation on a body of course, but this does help develop a certain sensitivity of touch.

Now sit with either your hands or your forearms resting tensionless on the table top, with your elbows over the edge. Let the weight of gravity on your elbows transmit through your forearms to your hands and fingers.

As a variation allow your body to bend backward from the waist, creating even more of a drag through your hands.

You will discover that the message is most clear to those hands that are soft and relaxed and alert to all the innuendos.

Begin dragging your hands across the desk, without actually allowing them to move. Ever-so-gradually. Ever-so-slowly. Feel the friction build.

Notice the multitude of events that occur within your skin before any outward movement occurs. Let your fingertips register the movement of tissue within its casing as it slowly separates itself from the grasp of friction.

Now let the weight of your hand shift slowly forward. Feel the increasing pressure buildup of internal structures pushing against the ends of your fingers. Shift your explorations from table top to living body and repeat the same maneuvers.

Unlike the table, this new playground has a multiplicity of sheets. Focus on a single one of them. Visualize the fascial sheath under your hands as your sheet upon the table. Search out restrictions of free movement exactly as you did with the coin.

Place your client on her back with you sitting by her head, your hands resting lightly on each side of her chest.....and slowly embark on a fascial drag. If this plane is free from restriction the pull should feel equal under both of your hands. Repeat the same maneuver with the weight of her shoulders resting in your hands.

Permit this same relaxed sensitivity to introduce you throughout the fascial network. **Feel for the sound of friction.** Seek out the coin, look at its size. Is it a penny or a quarter or a pocket full of change?

Alter your hand placement and visualize this restriction in three dimensions. Gauge its depth and its shape and its size and its density and if you can pick up additional information such as color and emotional tone so much the better.

With a little practice the process becomes second nature, and you are able to continuously monitor the state of the fascia from wherever you happen to have your hands on, or around, the body.

The tracts of constriction become more and more visible with less and less conscious effort. The time may come when you can sense their presence and location from across the room.

Yes, I do know people who can do this. The secret is to release your restrictions and open yourself to the music of your own body as well as to that of your client. Listen closely for all the rhythms. And you may hear the music of life.

Each rhythm speaks about the state of the entire instrument. The **rhythm of the breath** alone tells of excitement and emotion and energy and stress...and winks to us slyly when the ego pulls our leg.

Breath is a wondrous interpreter for our explorations. It is so very articulate that some of our bodyworker brothers and sisters use it as their exclusive guide and turn out absolutely magnificent work. Breath travels a giddy path that can take us to the stars and beyond.

The patterns of each of the guides have seemingly endless dimensions to them. Examine the breath. Notice first if it seems to be a natural pattern as opposed to a learned one. Possibly it has been imposed by some outside expectations. Whatever its character, it is certainly not there by accident.

What does this breathing pattern accomplish for your client?

* Does she use the breath to get in touch with her feelings or to hide from them?

* How much of her body participates with her breathing? What are the limits of this participation?

* Do the body parts harmonize in the exercise? Or is there dissonance? Does the breath skip over some areas, leaving still points as islands in a sea of movement?

Dance with the Guru

* Do the ribs expand on the intake one from the other, or does the rib cage merely imitate a slab of dead beef that rides atop a pulsating balloon? What are the rhythmic elements in this dance of the breath?

We may listen to the **rhythm of the heart** from anywhere on the body, or off the body as well, far off the body. It's good practice to adopt the circulatory system as one of your valued allies. You can use it as both a guide to the general state of the body as well as an indicator of specific and regional troubled areas.

The devas of this circulatory system call out to us and lead us down spectacular pathways. When I listen carefully and heed their instructions we get on first-rate together.

We accomplish much in what I consider to be a cozy relationship, but for some who specialize in the pulses, the relationship is even more intimate and grand. I have a bodywork comrade who uses a pulse as I would a telephone. She talks directly with the organ of her choice. I listened in on one such conversation and experienced my own kidneys for the first time. My first conscious physical experience with those hard working little warriors and since overhearing them I appreciate their efforts more than ever.

I have more than a nodding acquaintance with several of these pulses, but I know specialists who consider twenty-eight of them as their intimate friends. I have heard of still others who subdivide the pulses into thirty-two distinct messengers, each with specific qualities to distinguish it from its siblings.

While I hear circulatory melodies these colleagues must surely listen to symphonies. (I also know that thirty-two is just the beginning of the list.)

What enriches my ensemble and takes it to the heights is the **rhythm of the cerebral spinal fluid** pulsating through the dural tube. The craniosacral system can be our telephone to the very core of the body.

The system also maintains bodywide fascial connections that allow us to tune in directly to virtually any area of the body at all.

This rhythmic impulse is traditionally palpated by way of the cranium. It speaks the language of symmetry, flavored by a variety of regional nuances. Listen to the spirit. It showers us with a continuous rain of pulsative feedback. It's the compression itself calling to us: "Here I am. Over here if you please!"

We can use this rhythmic impulse as a telescope with a view directly down the dural tube. We can identify deep restrictions through an asymmetrical drag that makes itself known during cranial respiration. In time some practitioners come to the point of placing their hands lightly on the cranium or the neck and looking directly down the tube. From there they may progress to visualizing these restrictions before they palpate them, and to monitoring the dural tube with their hands placed anywhere at all on the body, and then with their hands not even on the body at all. It's always just a matter of awareness, you know.

Every single muscle all throughout the body emits a pulsation that stems from a tide of rhythmic contractions relentlessly stalked by relaxation and elongation.

Every Organ adds its own internal pulsations to the continual tide of palpable movement that is ever present everywhere, excepting of course, those traumatized areas where the muscular and visceral voices have been dampened and compressed to the point of imperceptibility.

The muscle speaks to us quite clearly about the immediate state of its health. As we ease restriction from its environment, it raises its amplitude like a surging wave, and we experience a pulsation where there was none before.

What you are experiencing is **a healing pulse,** a voice directly from the devas of the muscle. You are in the presence of the healing process itself.

However, the voice of any rhythm is influenced in some degree by the voices of *each* of the other rhythms. We probably never hear a pure pulsation in its most pristine form. Each of them impinges and is impinged upon in return.

Listen to one and you hear echos of all the others. Which might indicate that it's appropriate to consider them en masse.

I know of one European training program that would begin with the trainees spending their first few months just laying their hands on a body in front of them and listening through a stethoscope. They had no instructions other than to see what they might find. No one told them what to expect. Their task was to find out for themselves what might be there.

Some of these practitioners now use the **peristaltic movements** of the digestive tract as their primary guru. Movements which make an excellent guiding force for they accurately reflect the state of the entire body.

The message is that, as we learn the language, as we learn to listen, we may find ourselves overhearing discourses from even more of the physiological activities...from all those that want to be heard.

All we ever really need is a quiet, non-intrusive blending with our client...coupled with an unconditional acceptance of all that her body tells us, for the body does not like to be taken lightly.

The number and source of potential guides is seemingly endless. For efficiency's sake avail yourself of all the possibilities. We have bodywork siblings out there with senses that are uniquely acute. They can pick up tracts that are still invisible to the rest of us.

There are some who receive distinctive information in a very singular manner. If it's you who sees and interprets patterns of sound or color ranging throughout the body, patterns that others can't even imagine...then treasure this information, don't discard it. Teach the rest of us to appreciate it too. Yes, there are many who use shifting color patterns or tone scales as effective guides for their work.

So many body spirits try to contact us through so many vehicles. If we would only listen. All we have to do is listen.

Dance with the Guru

Some of the brothers and sisters can **see, hear, feel, even smell energy patterns.** Others can talk with the auras, or see directly into the body as though it were transparent, or dialogue directly with a specific organ or system. Some can communicate with the body in ways even they can't explain.

It pleases me that I have been able to work with all of the above, and we always seem to arrive at the same platform following different routes. And, no matter what you have heard, bodies do appreciate multiple and compatible fields of energy working on them at the same time. When we zero in on a compression with a comrade, the guides not only serenade us, they sing grand opera to us!

The devas are at your service.
Ready? Aye, Ready!....so go ahead...

Dance with your Guru!

Bodymagic..........

....*The Secret Revealed*

Everything you have ever learned is now prologue. This is the first time you have ever encountered a body exactly like this one. This body today is not like any other body you have ever seen, it's not even now like it was itself yesterday. Every-thing has shifted and continues shifting even now. Einstein once said: "Something's moving!" It certainly is.

I have worked on countless bodies that looked somewhat like this one and all that I learned from the others will help me now. But only as possibilities. I cannot do exactly the same with this body as I ever did with any other.

The contract is quite specific about this. There is a special clause about the magical promise of bodywork that becomes visible only as we honor the absolute uniqueness of this body. Unconditionally, without reservation.

For the client the magic is that of a fresh start. A completely cognizant re-beginning.

We may have consciously forgotten the knocks of life, but our body remembers. It compresses them into compact masses and maintains them as our biological

145

diaries. Our hurts and sorrows tightly embraced in living prisons, all in the name of love and survival, all to protect us from our own archaic nightmares.

Once this tissue is abused it tends to forget its early promise. It recalls nothing more than today's rigidity. It's our job to help it physically remember its heritage, to provide it with an actual experience, to help it recall how it is to live once again in the Shangri-la of self-determination.

Which is all in the dance. Movements have the incredible ability to expunge these memories in a shower of rhythm. The melody unshackles the drama. The indomitable tissue takes it from there and the original experience becomes complete. There is no longer anything for the tissues to hold on to.

Elbow room! That's what we're after here. Search out the holding pattern, that chronic compression which is also called stress, and strike the chains.

* **Wrap** yourself around an area of decreased flexibility and teach it to dance, slowly, and literally.

* See that compression over there? **Tickle its fancy,** literally tickle it, and watch it wiggle. Remind it of its innate ability to move, and give it some space to move in.

* It's called Liberation and this is your sergeant major: **Lift.**

It's also called the strategy of success.

Lift the tissue.

It's never anything other than this!

Just lift the tissue.

Even if you can't understand how this could be possible, think lift.

Even if you can't understand how this could be practical, think lift.

Think....of lifting the tissue out of compression.

It's a truth that may not be immediately self-evident. You will be sure to encounter a bodyworker somewhere apparently pressing his weight directly onto a bone, compressing tissues hapless enough to be trapped in the middle. However, this may be more appearance than reality. He may not actually be compressing what lies beneath his hands. The chief element of compression is a compacting of tissue. When two forces slide by each other there is no compaction. There is separation. Separation of tissue from bone, of tissue from tissue.

Separation, Decompaction, Lift.

(On the other hand it could be compression you witness. You could be in the presence of the dreaded Masher himself.)

A mechanical principle of all effective bodywork ...possibly the prime principle...is: **Don't Compress, Lift.**

Let this reality absorb into your hands as well as your mind. The client will tell you about it. Compression hurts.

Well of course there is an exception to this rule. Did you expect any different? A frozen area that resists movement, such as an old rusty joint, may sometimes benefit from a gentle and rhythmic addition of down weight as an incentive toward internal movement. There will be a slight release followed immediately by a lifting movement. So maybe it's not really an exception at all, just a bank shot.

Lifting can take the form of a **stretch.** But be careful. Taken too far too fast the stretch becomes a distortion, and moves into the probability of overextension and the tearing of the tissue. Nevertheless, stretch remains a most effective method of working. It travels in a spiral and the secret is in the speed, or the lack of it, and in the direction, and in the course of the angulation.

Stretch reaches out and calls to even the most desolate of areas. It has the potential to directly affect the most stubborn of tissue compressions, to release those abandoned twinges of the past kept in the deepest of memory dungeons. Dungeons that in the not-so-long ago were considered untouchable. But this is the dawn of enlightenment. Our sphere of influence is all pervasive and nothing in this body is beyond our reach.

It may sound like we are talking of two different techniques. First we sent the tissues spiraling into themselves, and now we are stretching them out. A coming together and a moving apart. **A pulsation**. These are not two separate events at all, just one. Each can be found lurking in the outer corners of the other. Each contains all the elements of the other with only a slight shift in focus.

Superficial tissue responds well to a combination stretch-and-feed technique. As we create a pull on either side of our working site, the tissue within becomes highly suggestible. We can orchestrate minute and specific changes between these stretching vectors by feeding tissue into itself. The hands do the stretching while the fingers do the feeding. (Actually any combination of body parts will do.)

With the very same hold, without changing our hands, we can alter the shape and direction of the spiral and extend its influence to cover as small or as large or as deep an area as we might wish.

Exact applications will differ with the client, but the principles remain universal. They apply not only to soft tissue but to joints as well. Which also need our attentions; they too become compacted. The soft tissue surrounding the joint must be considered as part of the complex. We must address all aspects of the unit, spreading our influence throughout the joint and into the bone itself. We are changing the environment which changes the chemistry, and thereby we influence all of the elements.

Consider the joint itself. Imagine there's a fluid endogenous to the joint, that serves primarily in a protective capacity, as a lubricant and as a shock absorber. Imagine that this fluid is encased in a container of silly putty. If we push rhythmically on the outside, we compress and release the fluid within to create waves of movement, which become our working tool within the joint. A decompression from within. But if we move too fast or with too much pressure the joint will simply freeze up on us.

There is a very simple guideline for working with joints. **Stroke the socket** from every possible direction.

Guide the wave around every corner and probe into every cranny. Open up the socket and stretch it out. Open it up completely.

S-t-r-e-t-c-h it all the way out.

A rusty joint likes to be eased into the process. First we gently compress it into itself until it releases, and only then do we help it decompress. With a very rusty joint we may choose to more actively aid the process by a rhythmic dance of in-and-out and around-and-about, tracing all the contours of the socket. A dance to improve both the chemistry and the stability of the joint.

The secret of this dance is to **listen** and to **lift** and to **remind** the joints of what a genuine joy free movement can be.

Lift out the compressions and encourage the dance.

Compressions also serve as jails, and any one of them may confine an emotional hurricane. Rage or terror or who-knows-what may be lurking just behind the door. The ego knows its business. It uses compression to dampen the emotions and protect us from the storm. Recognize this for what it is.....Drama.

Now we can whisper to the tissue that this is all for the history books. This is a new day today. So release this suppression-by-compression, hold the door open for it and cheer it along its way. Tissues appreciate all the little courtesies. They always feel so easy and so soft following a cleansing.

This is why a body changes so dramatically after an emotional catharsis. It is such a relief for the tissues to take a breath. It takes constant energy to suppress an emotion. It becomes an ever present stress on the body that affects the breathing mechanism itself. The emotion may be small, but the burden on the system never is. Let it out. Relieve the body of this excessive effort and the body smiles and straightens itself up and assumes a new appearance, or reclaims an old and forgotten one.

Of course the body looks better. It is better. It's visually and measurably taller...and leaner. As a body compresses it shortens, as it decompresses it lengthens. Along with the increased height comes an emerging sense of grace.

The world can't help but notice. Maybe they can't quite put their finger on it, but they know something has changed. "You seem happy today" ...or healthy, or attractive, or well rested. They are right on all counts. For a fact, you are each of these.

A fundamental factor of limitation may be the client's own lack of awareness. Our job is to help her recognize and release her unconscious physical and emotional holding patterns. Release her from outdated restraints and let her definitions expand. Help her redefine herself.

It's her parade! We follow and mobilize the troops, and lead the cheers. We illuminate the path and shout encouragement to a harmony of function and structure.

We do all this by releasing some very depressing restrictions. By decompressing all those old compressions. By planting the germ of a rhythm within a tissue that already yearns to be moving. By listening and exchanging confidences.

By example.

Healthy tissue is always on the move. Unrestricted movement of layer upon layer. Our workplace is on movable tissue that is floating on a movable shelf, that is itself on another movable shelf...and the dance goes on. Our work addresses these ever moving relationships.

In the public mind, bodywork is equated with deep tissue massage (it is certainly that, but it's much more besides). The tendency is to see deep pressure work and deep tissue work as one and the same.

Actually they are opposites. *The relationship of the depth of the work to the force applied is literally inverse.* The more pressure forced on the body, the stronger it resists. Heavy pressure may loosen the outer layers (or it may not), but the very deep tissues protect themselves by compressing even tighter. Under a perceived attack the body will surrender its superficial areas, while retrenching and re-grouping its energies, and making its stand closer to the core, where its deeper secrets are stored. The ego trades off release of one area for more security in another.

The secret of working deeply within the body may be found **in the exhale.** If you are not getting the work done, check your breathing patterns. It's not possible to hold your breath and work deeply on another person. So just exhale and let it all come out.

The deepest work is actually the most effortless. It comes with following the body, understanding its

language, and honoring its wishes. It comes with following the guides and allowing their rhythmic pulsations to open up the area.

Exhale...and experience your relaxation. Continue breathing as you place your hands on the back of the client's head and ever so gently traction her occiput. A few ounces of pull at best (some say grams, not ounces), and **wait.** It will be a wait well worth your while. Once you have experienced the dural tube disengage and float freely within a slowly pulsating rhythm, there is no longer any question of what deep work really looks like.

Our innermost areas won't talk much under duress. Our dural tube not at all. You can coax it but you can't force it. It lives up to its name. It's one tough mother.

* If your hands discern a snag in this tube, then ride the pulsations and follow it, or take it, to the **edge of its arc** and ever so gently apply a holding traction. And wait. And witness its quiet struggle to expand its outer limits and reclaim its barren wastelands.

Let your rhythms merge with those of your client. Follow where her tissues lead and, when requested, gently overtake and supplant them. One moment you follow and the next you lead. Two blending imperceptibly into one, and it becomes a dance without a leader.

We can cultivate this quality of communication by taking a body unit on a passive stroll throughout all its arcs of motion. A slow, leisurely stroll. Along the way we may pass a particular point where the motion speeds up each time it approaches, as if to go by a graveyard as quickly as possible. At this point a spasm-like jerk overrides the passivity of the unit and always at the same location.

We are feeling the face of fear. The tissue is scared at a very basic level. But as frightened as it is, it still entrusts us with the key to the vault. The body is apprehensive but still directs us. Return with it to the graveyard...and slow all the way down...and stop...and sit for a while on top of the spasm...and allow the soul to unwind its scars.

Have the courage to wait. To just sit and witness, no matter what goblin sticks up its head. Have the courage to see it through. It's here that we earn our trust.

We earn it through our touch. Through hands that reflect the state of our mind and the truth of our soul. Through an unflappable acceptance of what is. And for this to occur, we must remain as aware of our own body as we are that of our client's.

The secret, as always. is awareness. Focus on your working hands. Notice if they work together, or if each is on its own. Does one primarily feed tissue to the other that does the actual work, or do they share the work equally? This is not about the right way to work. There is no single right way to work. This is about awareness.

The value is in the looking.

So look. Very specifically.

Where is the primary change occurring in this body under your hands and where are the secondary changes? This is an ongoing question that requires ongoing answers.

Bodymagic

Your hands can remain in conscious contact with each other at all times, no matter how far apart they are on the body. They are always aware of the work the other does, as well as the work that they do together. It's only a matter of sensitizing yourself.

You can use any part of the body as a lever to feed tissue and movement into any other part. You can use both hands as levers at the same time, feeding the movement into any place in between. You can change levers and speak to slightly different aspects of the situation. You can change the angle of your spiral and address completely different aspects. And all throughout the process your hands remain in constant communication with each other.

As an exercise place your hands on both sides of a thigh. Wherever your hands contact tissue, use that placement as your lever. From there **angle the natural rhythms** of the body into various fascial roadways.

First let the tissue take you where it will. Then actively, but slowly, **channel** the rhythmic movement of the tissues into the hip socket, and then into the pelvis, and then into the abdominal cavity. If your movement abruptly stops at the entrance, settle there and wait and slyly caress the barrier. Entice it first out of your way, and then out of the body.

"Louie, I think this is the beginning of a beautiful friendship" ...or at least of a deep and profound communication. Its strength is in the slow and the quiet. The secret word is subtle.

In the case of a joint, feed the movement inward and probe for restrictions. Explore the contours of the socket and invite the squatters out. Movement itself is a force for de-restriction. The working principle is that this not be hurried or forced. The very movement that frees can be misused and create even further restrictions.

The point is that, with pulsation as our tool, we can use anything as a handle, and our reach is unlimited. We can mediate between feuding neighbors no matter where they live.

When the body is shown a touch that is both aware and compassionate, it recognizes a friend and permits us to work from the inside out as well as from the outside in.

We can talk with all aspects of the body during the same session, the Law of the Onion notwithstanding. Be assured that, as we truly follow the body, such restrictions on our work no longer apply.

There is no single way to approach an objective. So experiment. Make your overtures from every angle. From the East as well as the West.

If the dural tube is your interest, then talk to it from both the sacrum and the occiput. Individually at first, and then from both points together, and then from various intermediate points. Wherever you place your hand the effect will differ to some extent.

Select any section of the body that attracts your attention, and passively position it to match a three dimensional posture that it already favors. Help it to move into this posture of ease, help it to exaggerate the posture, and then quietly, without forcing, help it to hold the exaggeration.

Within this exaggeration the song of the tissues will exert itself. The area will sing a little and start to shuffle its feet. An incipient dance emerges. Become its shadow, adding only a barely perceptible emphasis. **Encourage the movement to expand itself.** As it claims an adjacent area, secure it and allow the body to unwind itself even further.

This is the secret. **Listen well, and follow, and most of all get yourself out of the way.** It is neither your responsibility nor your place to decide what treatment to use. It's the client's decision. Follow the dictates of her tissue. Befriend her body by helping it to unwind according to its own dictates. The unwinding may be either regionally or as a complete unit. It's her choice.

Your results are more than a little dependent on you enjoying yourself. So do so! Take pleasure in the unwrapping process. In the unveiling of a long suppressed inner joy. Your pleasure communicates and becomes highly contagious. As it is shared, it expands. You become witness to the natural rhythm of movement and health dancing together in time.

The secrets of bodywork all manifest within this common ground you create with your client.

The magic comes with recognizing that each of us is a metaphor of the other.

So who's treating who here anyway?

The Promise...

...and The Possibility

"That's as far as it can go."

A successful and physically active middle aged man is speaking about his right shoulder. The pain has been unrelenting for years and his range of motion is severely restricted. He is bothered by the restriction more than he is by the pain. "It's been that way for years. I've had every treatment there is and they all say the same thing: *Learn to live with it.*"

It's a libretto that's all too familiar to bodyworkers. What can be done has been done. The possibilities have been exhausted. There is nothing more that anyone can do. *Learn to live with it.*

This man didn't buy it. He continued making the rounds and got lucky. He stumbled across someone who had a friend who had experienced remarkable success with a procedure called bodywork and here he is.

This was what he said before bodywork. So what does he say about his condition now?

Well for one thing, he doesn't miss the pain at all. For another, he has a completely normal range of motion throughout his shoulder and arm, which was his primary concern in the first place.

You've heard the then, and you've heard the now, but what happened in between?

There was a bodyworker and a client together in a room, and somewhere within this framework a healing took place.

How did it happen and who did it?

In my experience it's always the client who creates the healing. As bodyworkers we create the context. We clear the road, we expedite, we lead the cheers, and we witness for our client as he takes advantage of the opportunity and reclaims his own health.

My results as a bodyworker improve as I keep in mind **a basic truism:** When the client and I are in a room by ourselves, there is only one expert present, and it isn't me. I'm the student in that room and I have to listen carefully. I have to follow instructions and remember to get out of my own way.

And I must not lose sight of the direct link between the belief and the result. My work can't come from a basis of my beliefs, not and get the results that I want. I have to suspend my judgements and take what is present. Like it says above, I have to get out of my own way.

I know that our language defines, and ultimately limits, our reality. I can listen to your language, as one bodyworker to another, and predict your results. Our upper-most limits are always very clearly stated.

Monitor your own professional communications and notice what limitations you and your client may place upon yourselves.

The potential depends on just how much each member of this partnership can open himself up to. How much of you, the bodyworker lives in a different era, and how much of you the client is holding on to your past. Notice how much the two of you are willing to work together in present time.

We need this foundation to experience the intoxicating freedom that comes with letting go. Not only of structural holding patterns, but of any holding patterns not absolutely appropriate to our present coordinates.

Body freedom can only be experienced in the now. Never in the holding. You can not squeeze grace or ease and have them remain graceful and easy for long. The joy of the body is in the movement of the moment, and movement can not be caged and still remain a movement. Try to trap a movement and all you have is a corpse. The moment has passed and the joy has faded.

The secret of our work is to never imprison a memory, no matter how great the experience may be. Life is for living in abundance. When you let go of something wonderful, rest assured that something even more wonderful will come to take its place.

The words are easy to say but a bit more difficult to practice. They grate against even the slightest residue of a limitation mentality that still remains to haunt us.

The seed is not the same as the corn. As we hold the

seed, we hold the promise of corn. But it's only the promise. Which may be enough to satisfy your dreams. If we plant the seed we may lose it and so, all too often, we choose to hoard our seeds. The promise remains only a dream.

It was of a dream-like evening in Los Angeles when this profound truth came hammering at the door of my scarcity consciousness. A truth that would not be denied. I was in a group rebirthing situation, a process of conscious and connected breathing, with more than a hundred congenial souls sharing my floor space.

I felt strangely at peace in this unusual setting. I connected to my breathing and felt my body and mind meet and sink into a comfortable rhythm, which led me almost immediately into a sustained Reichian orgasmic experience, my energy centers connecting with a sustained vibration echoing throughout my body.

This was not an unfamiliar space to me, I love the feeling of my body frolicking within a rapture. I wallowed in my bliss and I held it tight. This was as close to Nirvana as I could come. I could stay here forever.

But a rebirther saw me and was all too quickly present with the suggestion that I was holding on, that I could let go and just follow my breath. I resisted only momentarily (much to my own surprise). The suggestion was unwelcomed but I followed it. This time my breath took me all the way back to my original nursery situation, a setting that was not familiar, but was not completely unfamiliar either.

I reacquainted myself with the suppressed memory where, surrounded by the clamor of all the other newborns, I had once been completely and ultimately alone.

And I remembered it all. And once more in this lifetime I committed the same act of incredible bravery that I had once before. I chose life.

I felt supremely humiliated by my obstetrician, I had been treated high-handedly by all those surrounding my birth yet, despite this primal experience of helplessness in a hostile world, I chose life.

And now I experienced the wonder and awe of this most commendable action all over again, I luxuriated in pride at my own bravery, sumptuously pleased with myself. And I held on to my feelings. I wanted to hold on forever. This became my summit. Higher than I had ever been. A feeling nothing could surpass.

And then Sondra Ray, an exquisite healer, as well as founder of the Loving Relationships Trainings, came by and saw and understood. She prodded me with a whisper, a gentle inquiry about a blockage in my stomach.

"What are you holding there? What is its purpose?"

I silently screamed a scream big enough to fill the room. "Can't you even see where I'm at! Are you so dense you can't even recognize enlightenment when you look it right in the face!"

On the outside I remained quiet while I considered her question. Somewhat reluctantly I released my hold on this ultimate high and breathed into my blockage. The breath itself inquired of its purpose and got an immediate answer. The world was unsafe! I needed to hold on to something.

I needed that blockage. It prevented me from having everything I wanted. If I had everything life would be just too good and God would surely punish me for being so pretentious. If I didn't hold on to something I would burst open and explode into nothingness. Not even a trace of the me would remain.

Sondra reminded me that I could so have everything, that the more I had, the safer the world would become for me, and the more love that would be available to me.

There was a truth in these words that I could not resist (although I tried). My body acknowledged it first, and then my head. And I breathed into the affirmation and my body tingled from head to toe. And of course I held on to my tingling.

This time I was aware of my holding, I felt it and I let it go. I did it by myself without outside prodding. I must be learning something. I shared my silent affirmation with my nursery mates. "The more we have, the safer the world is for us, for all of us, and the more love there is for us too." Wonderous! So of course I held on to the wonder. I heard myself arguing that I just couldn't go any higher anyway. And I knew I lied.

Just trust the universe. It was easier this time. I went with my breath, and it directed me to the true purpose of bodywork. We are here to expand this brotherhood, to make the promise available to us all, to recreate bodies that are increasingly receptive to the dance, to help each body claim its potential...and by that exact amount the world will be closer to claiming its own dream.

I breathed myself into a state of complete cellular orgasm. A life in the midst of celebrating life itself, and this time I didn't even hesitate. I made no effort at all to stop and hold what I had. I just enjoyed it. I continued my breathing and connected with the divine potential of our work with the bodily knowledge that what we are really doing is helping others contact their own divinity. That self-obscured divinity that lives within.

And through helping others connect with their divinity we encounter our own magnificence.

Which is a treasure to be experienced but not held. It lives within its movement. We can see its pulsations, we can hear them and we can taste them, but we can't hold them. This movement is the stuff of life itself, and it comes on the breath, and of course the movement and the breath are ultimately of the same fabric. Just as breathing and bodywork are the true Gemini.

We are speaking of totality. Which is to speak of potential. Just as to speak of the body is to speak of the mind, and of the emotions, and of the spirit. Our thought patterns underscore and support all our other patterns. The potential starts and grows easiest within a fertile and unfettered mind.

A number of years ago two leaders of a religious community came to me for bodywork, and said their purpose was to cleanse their karma. They surely must have known what a confirmed fool they were talking with. I snickered to myself that, while I was willing to work on their bodies, their karmas had to look out for themselves.

Shortly thereafter, much to my own wonderment, I went on a spur-of-the-moment fast that extended through ten days. There was no thought behind it. It happened a day at a time. It just happened that each day, for ten days, I just happened to choose not to eat.

It was kind of nice not to eat. I had never been on a fast before. I lost excess weight and my body felt cleansed.

Two weeks later these same two leaders mentioned that they had both been on a fast. Yes, they admitted, as a matter of fact, they had initiated mine.

It made perfect sense to me. If you are going to use an instrument you may as well clean it up a bit. I felt no resentment. I didn't even feel manipulated. Somehow I felt honored, and grateful. Since then many others have come to me to work on their karmas. I don't snicker anymore.

My experience with the client-bodyworker relation-ship suggests that it is not as haphazard, or as casually assumed, as I once thought it was. It's even possible there may be a larger-than-obvious purpose behind it.

I've found that, as we work on the physical expres-sion of karma with our clients, we often look to our own karmas as well. On at least one occasion I met mine head on...

My body felt an immediate and strange sense of unease as the pleasantly attractive client came into my offices. Her excuse was a life-long pain under her right shoulder blade. Of course she had exhausted all the usual avenues of treatment.

The expert consensus was that it was all in her mind. Be that as it may, there was clearly something palpable in her tissues as well. To my fingers it felt exactly like old scar tissue.

Over the next few weeks we both began to recognize that this pain had all the characteristics of a wound, of a very ancient wound. Piece by piece the nature of the wound made itself known to us.

An arrow had made this wound, definitely an arrow. An arrow from another time and another place. Yet the memory of the arrow was still present, hiding unresolved in this tissue under the shoulder blade. There was nothing for me to do but remove the arrow.

I felt the fear and the sorrow trapped within the flesh. I felt the release as my hands dismantled the compression. A vision from the past overtook and engulfed us both, and we knew exactly how the arrow got there in the first place, who put it there and why. It seemed only appropriate that it would also be me who removed it. The transaction was complete. She hasn't had even a trace of a shoulder problem since.

This was not a once in a lifetime event. Past life experiences are not that uncommon an occurrence during bodywork. My clients and I frequently discover that we have interacted together before this. Often through multiple life times.

Areas of the body severely frightened in a past life may be ultra vulnerable in this one. Underlying a present day condition may be another experience, further removed in time, but with a similar theme.

Like a record stuck in a groove the soul replays the same phrase over and over again as if to get it right. The fabled haunting melody recycling itself endlessly.

Body Secrets

Bodywork can break the cycle...and free the soul. That's the promise. Free this body from the past...no matter how far back that past may go.

The quality and direction of a life can shift slowly over an extended period of time, or instantaneously, or even outside of time altogether. A single session may change a life forever.

An attitude that is anchored in the structure is at the dictates of any movement passing through. Just as the structure and the movement are modified by the attitude. It's efficient to arrange your session around the weakest link in the chain. Just one session, and my politics changed completely and permanently.

The vehicle was the magical hands of Marion Rosen wrapped lightly around my head. We were in a courtyard where a tree shaded my eyes from the midday Berkeley sun. As her hands talked the courtyard slipped away from me at an ever accelerating pace. Her jet propelled table rocketed me over an ever broadening landscape. Over countryside such as I had never seen before, nor even imagined. This was not my landscape, not my scenery, not even my reality. It was a comic strip! A cross between Will Eisner and Marvel comics to be exact.

A primordial Marvel comics whizzing me faster and faster back through the coordinates of space and time. Faster and faster all the way back to the Big Bang. The original Big Bang that started it all. An awesome and inspiring event to witness, and I saw that I was there, and that you were there, and that all of us were there together.

And I was reminded that, when I first entered this world, all I wanted was to sing and to dance in joy and freedom, and from the very start they stepped all over my dreams, and continued stepping on them. I knew then that, from this point on, I would no longer do to another what they had done to me. And I knew their faces.

It was a different person who returned from that trip, a person with a different attitude and a different philosophy. The changes have lasted. I no longer rain on anyone's parade (I try not to). I withdrew my support from the process and the strength of the process depreciated by exactly that amount.

This one session changed my thought patterns and therefore my vote in the upcoming election. My behavior did an about face as it reflected the loosening of my cranial sutures. My rigid attitudes had been anchored in a rigid structure.

It's always rigidity vs flexibility.

Function and form chasing each other's tail. There is an Osteopathic Doctor blessed with an amazingly tranquil temperament and a quite considerable talent who lives on the coast of Florida with its warm and refreshing ocean breezes. Of course he's tranquil. It's easy to be tranquil in such a setting.

Not always! The way he tells it, it wasn't always this way. If nitpicking were an Olympic event, not so long ago he would have qualified as a world class competitor.

Then during a bodywork session he found himself across the table, on his back, with his feet nearly touching the floor on one side and his head on the other. A position that for one of his girth was obviously impossible. He heard a pop and experienced a release within his head. His sutures shifted, and apparently loosened his mellow bone, which has remained free to this day. (Of course there's a mellow bone, how else would you explain this metamorphosis?)

The promise goes on. Intervene in any one area of a life, and we inspire all the related areas. A movie producer came in sporting an ingenious series of slouches designed, quite successfully, to make him appear smaller than his real height. A quite substantial height at that. He was living his life smaller than his structure intended.

As we worked he began unfolding. In structure and in function. It was only as he learned to claim every inch to which his structure was entitled, and claim it proudly, only then did he also learn to create Big Money Transactions. I mean BIG MONEY. As he lived big he behaved big. The most obvious practical rewards of expansion for him were monetary.

Another client came from out of state, wanting me to help him regrow his hair. He recounted how a friend of his had come to me completely bald and now had a full head of hair.

Ridiculous! I assured him it was no more than a silly coincidence. If I knew how to grow hair, I would start with my own. But somewhere along the line I must have released my limiting thoughts because through our work together he actually did grow a complete head of hair. He has not been the only one either. I sometimes wonder why it hasn't worked for me.

Imagine if you will, the wonder of witnessing a client as she claims a new body. An actual new body that is still somewhat alien and ill fitting. A body that she walked into, not that she was born into.

(These are not my beliefs, they are my experiences. Basically I am a doubter and I wish that I wasn't. It's such a limitation. But there is still some part of me that expects the universe to trick me, to suddenly wink and yell "Gotcha!" And that's why my hair isn't growing back.)

I watched her move into the unexplored corners of this new body with a combination of bodywork and breath. As I physically opened an area for her perusal, she breathed through all its corridors, cleaning out all the negative thoughts residing there. She wiggled the rest of the way in and shaped it to meet her unique specifications, and claimed it for her own. And her body felt great and just couldn't stop singing.

Consider this. A client comes to you who, among other things, wants to recreate an organ that has been surgically removed. Does this sound impossible to you?

If there were even the slightest possibility, what procedures would you use?

What the two of us used was connected breathing, and complete tissue micro-movements, and **a calling by**

name of all the elements that forced the organ to move out in the first place. Cleansing the house as it had never been cleansed before, completely expunging the past. We continue creating and recreating an absolutely safe environment and inviting her uterus to try once more, to come back on home. And at least one of those who has the ability to look directly into the body, says that is what appears to be happening.

As you can see my clients are more than just clients. They are my teachers. A few special clients are my spiritual teachers as well. When I work with them it's a relicensing seminar for my soul...and my professional education continues as well.

There is one who wants a body composed increasingly of pure energy and less of the more dense structural matter now present. She wants eventually to be composed completely of light with nothing to slow her down. Even at her present stage of development her tissues are unique. They radiate a quality of pure goodness.

She reminds me of the dream of Ida Rolf, who envisioned her work as the next step in the evolutionary process. A conscious step.

But the promise of bodywork exceeds all of the above. Clients continually show me that our potential is unbounded, unrestricted, and completely limitless. The limitations that I see are my own and they are mistakes in perception. Because if we can imagine it...it's out there for us....out there in the realm of possibility and it's just a matter of applying the proper mechanics.

The Physics of Spiritual Magic

......An Overlooked Element of Bodywork.

On reaching the Himalayas I found that all I knew about bodywork was only prologue. In this most appropriate of settings I saw my boundaries shatter and my limitations crumble as I experienced a perceptual shift in my basic understanding of the principles, the techniques, and even the purpose of bodywork, as the mechanics of the spiritual process marched relentlessly into conscious awareness.

As a student/teacher/practitioner of Body Harmony I am well aware that the tools at my disposal are only a fragment of those available, and that few if any of them are unique to Body Harmony. They have all been in practice sometime, somewhere in the world before. Unfortunately they have usually been practiced in isolation, kept separate from their spiritual brothers, their true natures obscured through various philosophical guises.

What was originally a unified whole had somehow become splintered, with each segment assigned to a different arena.

173

Precious fragments were held incognito behind the strong walls of semantic fortresses. Bodywork was never quite able to reach its full potential, it was like a symphony orchestra that had misplaced a few of its instruments. There was always a quiet residue of unfulfilled hunger left behind. What was needed was a soul to reissue a call of convocation.

Body Harmony evolved through the bringing together of these stray parts. The body of the work evolved long before the name, which didn't evolve at all, it just popped in on a direct channel through my lips, I personally had little to do with it.

...this particular Ashram was nestled in the Himalayan foothills near the border of Nepal. In an area of mountainous imperturbability that exudes a rare sense of clarity. Where the air bears no relationship to what I know in Los Angeles and the stars shine with a directness that makes it easy for one's perceptions to mirror the surrounding clarity.

My stay there was in a time out of sequence. In a context of now, where the immediacy of the moment was in constant contradiction to the surrounding timelessness. Small wonder that it was in such a paradoxical setting that I was made ready to receive one of the missing fragments, one of the greatest fragments of them all, the actual physical techniques to assist in the rising of the Kundalini. Or, to be more precise, the techniques for removing the impediments that keep the Kundalini down in the first place, a technology for clearing the road and allowing the parade to begin.

The Physics of Spiritual Magic

Such information is usually not offered lightly. One must be able to hear and to understand...so first I had to be prepared. My cup was full and running over, I had accumulated too much knowledge to be open to new and unfamiliar ego-threatening realities.

Ida Rolf's first words to me had been nothing so mundane as "Hello, I'm Ida Rolf." Our association began with..."The trouble with you is..." and my world became a notch less secure.

"The trouble with you is that you know too well how to make it happen. You better learn to let it happen!" She was right of course, she usually was, although it took me the better part of two decades to realize just how right she actually was.

But I had learned the lesson. I went ever more with the flow. I repeated the words, and I said the mantras and I let it go...or at least I thought I let it go. Actually I only loosened my grip a little.

I didn't live the words as much as I ran their vibrations through my lips. My trust in the Universe was neither total nor unquestioning, and now it came home, for here I was led to experience the distance between my words and my actions. I had to be quieted in order to listen and to understand reality.

Considering the other-worldliness of the setting, given the rapidity with which each of my personal bugaboos came up for a healing, I shouldn't have been surprised to be afforded the rare opportunity to do Body Harmony on an Indian Saint, on one in charge of an influential and multinational spiritual community.

I was honored to work on such a personage, of course, but what I didn't realize was that it was merely an illusion. I only thought that I was to work on him, in truth it was he who did the work on me. I placed my hands on his chest and in the placing my world shifted and could never again be as it was.

It wasn't that I didn't appreciate the wonderous tools left us by Ida Rolf and her fellow geniuses of the body. It's more that I came to understand her teachings on a cellular level. My tissues themselves glimpsed the absolute awesomeness of what she had been trying to create, and what she had only been able to allude to in a very oblique fashion. But that was an understanding that came later...in Delhi.

I lowered my hands onto the body before me and my world shifted and nothing ever looked quite the same as before. The quake accompanied the contact, the immediate contact.

I am accustomed to contacting a body in easy stages, avoiding any disturbance or hint of intrusion into my client's energy fields. I am accustomed to blending almost unnoticed with each succeeding energy layer until the two of us unite in a dance of tissue understanding. This is what I am accustomed to.

Why then did I find myself dive bombing this innocent chest before me? Why were my hands behaving more like a Kamikaze attack than a caress? Why in this of all moments, had my sensitivities so completely deserted me?

The Physics of Spiritual Magic

Within what should have been a very special moment I found myself committing exactly those sins that I warned against in all my introductory lectures. **I was entering this energy field with an attitude of knowing, rather than a spirit of exploration.** I tried to impose my considerable experience on this body before me, and found that it existed outside the bounds of my experience.

I had unwittingly programmed myself to allow successive barriers of energy to cushion the descent of my hands, and here no such artificial defense system was in effect...and this was only by way of introduction.

The process itself took on its own flow, but the session resembled no other session before it. At one point an extremely agitated madman burst, exploded is the more accurate word, into the room, gesticulating wildly, completely shredding the general tranquility, shattering the calm of all those present...with one notable exception. My client granted no acknowledgement to this person's spectacular entrance, even though the two of them were physically separated by only a few feet of open space.

Throughout the event I monitored the combined rhythmic patterns of my client's breath, circulatory system, and cerebral spinal impulse, and not one of them fluctuated in the slightest degree. He exhibited no startle reaction whatsoever, neither internal nor external.

But this was only an abstraction! This philosophical concept of perfect internal composure I had *heard* of, but I certainly didn't *believe* in it....and here it was!

Body Secrets

It seems that India has a tradition of the miraculous, a philosophical climate where such events don't need my agreement in order to have their way...and this was only the beginning.

...and I recalled once again those first words of Ida Rolf's..."You better learn to let it happen." I had learned the lesson....somewhat. I had learned to follow the tissues more than to lead them. I publicly acknowledged my results as a cooperative endeavor, I tried to lead and be led, to give and receive in equal measure, but somewhere along the line I had betrayed myself. In attempting to separate myself from the subjective, I had removed myself from the equation itself. I always wound up completely self sufficient. I seemed to be too keen to be leaned on, while never allowing myself to do the leaning. Just why did I need to live my life so completely in charge? Was I really so scared?

My hands on the saint reflected me back upon myself and I experienced the fundamental components of my own imbalances. I encountered them as inner physical rigidities that twisted my tissues into rigid attitudes and behaviors...as unnecessary personal limitations which compressed my unbridled spirit. Reflections which placed me in direct contact with the exact structures that condition all of our limiting thoughts and maintain all of our limiting behaviors.

Joyfully I danced with his tissues, as all the while they illuminated my own holding patterns, unsuspected patterns, patterns so very basic to my ego defenses that I had concealed their existence from any conscious consideration.

I shouldn't have been too surprised at this turn of events, for ever since I arrived, remnants of the past kept popping up to haunt me. All those defenses I had counted as my strengths, I began experiencing as only the limiting effects of a frightened ego.

For years I had voiced the concept of strength equalling flexibility. Truly I was accustomed to mouthing my ethics more than living them.

I found myself ingested into a process that bore no identifiable landmarks, I had no idea of the nature of the process nor where it might be taking me.

Working on this body before me, my own body began a rather mystifying detoxification process...which escalated by the moment into a state of total surrender.

An unfamiliar place it was, a place without strength or defense, without resistance, without reason, without pain...and especially **without the illusion of self sufficiency...or the myth of separation.**

Following this extraordinary session I retreated within, wrapping myself within a cocoon of a strangely quiet and pleasant stupor.

However, there was a treat on schedule for the very next day, a visit to an extremely holy temple. My intention was to remain behind and rest, but somehow my body chose a different course, and as if through a haze I observed myself getting on the back of the bus for a trip that could be only a drain on my already nonexistent resources. The ride was long, and uncomfortable, and unendurably muggy.

When the bus did stop there remained yet another obstacle, a path up an impossibly steep mountain, maybe a twenty minute walk for your average weekend athlete, but for me it was the Matterhorn.

I collapsed gratefully across the back seat of the bus. It was quiet and in the shade and represented the total fulfillment of all my immediate dreams. My senses were unanimous in dictating that I stay in the back of that bus exactly where I was.....

.......but when the saint appeared and said "walk!" ...I walked. Up that hill I struggled... five...ten...fifteen agonizing feet...determined, intrepid...

Until there was but one choice. Stop and sit down...or pass out and fall down. I no longer could marshal the necessary reserves to continue standing, much less walking.

The saint reached down and ever-so-lightly touched my elbow, and raised me up, and together we marched up the hill and into the temple...and quite briskly as a matter of fact. We overtook several groups of hikers along the way.

It was not so much that he helped me up the hill, it was more that he carried me up, completely, totally carried me up by the support of a hand that was so gentle and so understanding, a hand that was more of a suggestion, more of a remembrance than a physical support.

Why was I so strangely touched?

Why did I have to fight back the tears even as he touched me?

And why did I cry for weeks afterwards whenever I related the incident?

I suppose that even then I must have recognized the gift I was being prepared to receive. I must have known on some level, that I was receiving another chance, being placed back into the equation once again.

The schedule called for one final trek, a magical one by all accounts, both my head and my emotions yelled Go! But by then my body existed in a state of grace that required absolute obedience. It asserted itself not by request but by decree. My ego had little choice in the matter for when the body and the soul want something bad enough, they absolutely will have their way...and that is that!

...instead I spent two days in a New Delhi hotel, two days alone and flat on my back, in the traditional posture of receptivity (it turned out), weak to the point of lethargic but without noticeable discomfort...The only purpose of my existence now it seemed was to witness the strange pictures that began unfolding within my head.

...two full days...alone...flat on my back in a hotel room...not sick...not even hungry. There were nights in the mountains when I dreamed of the incomparable delights of chocolate ice cream....and now given the opportunity I didn't even pick up the phone and call room service....and there was a TV that I never turned on and magazines and books that I never opened.

...two days unlike any other days I have ever experienced, just lying on my back completely open...open to what I had no idea. I didn't even judge the experience, which to a mind that doubts can be a wonderous blessing.

...when in the very center of my forehead there appeared an expectant tingling...in that strange area where the third eye is said to reside...and it lit up blue, but what a blue! ...a blue of unsuspected and unimagined depth, beautiful like no other blue before....which could be nothing less than the fabled third eye itself....in which I had never believed, but which I never again could deny the reality of...and I was only mildly surprised.

From the depths there appeared the most extraordinary and otherworldly face. It may have been flesh, it may have been marble.

Flesh or stone, male or female or both within the other...impossible to decipher. A face not bound by the definitive restrictions of either/or. A face of authority, absolute authority, shining from within with an intensity that was at once powerful and awesome and peaceful and wonderful and, most of all, absolutely empowering to the beholder.

Initially it was one face that eventually displayed three other equally magnificent aspects of itself, and I lay and beheld the power. In a state of ecstasy I watched a movie unfold, a panoramic movie of the only partially understood possibilities of bodywork, of the enormous possibilities inherent in a truly free body.

The Physics of Spiritual Magic

The information was transmitted as a unit, in a totality and a completeness that made words cumbersome and unnecessary, transmitted in multilayered pictographs that were equally accessible to every one of my senses. I saw it visually and I felt it both actively and passively in the tissues of my hands and the cells of my body, I gathered it in on a cellular and an energy level, on an emotional level and an intellectual level.....all my senses united in the gathering and the understanding of the data. Including senses unknown to my rational mind. Senses that I had dared not suspect were available to me.

I had always intuited the possible wonders of the bodywork process even before I witnessed them, but there was usually something vague lurking around the edges.

Now I witnessed the exact physics of the unwinding process. I rode the tail of the rising Kundalini and witnessed first hand all the accumulated roadblocks we have singularly and collectively erected along the way. I nodded to the inhibiting musculature that slows and hinders and detours the process. I looked directly into the varied faces of strength and gentleness and knew that both are requisite for these proceedings.

It was information transmitted outside of any familiar time frame, possibly instantaneous. But my rational mind needed time to replay the movie, needed an interval to reflect and to wonder, and the space to make the initial attempts at verbalizing the process, time and space to integrate two full days of wonder and contentment, when I was without ego and connected to the Universe.

Oh yes, all that I had studied was indeed only prologue...all to help me absorb this information, to help me use it and to pass it along...this is what it was all about...it was all one trail leading me to this moment of recognition...this moment of grateful remembrance...

...and the process of Body Harmony that has always existed in a state of flux, moved further outside the boundaries of limitation and dipped its toes into the currents of infinity.

The physics of the process are not divisible, the magic is to be found within the interactions themselves, not within or between the units. It's not a matter of what you do but of how you do it and one thing you can not do is stand outside of the process. **You are the process.**

The task of Body Harmony, at this stage, is the transmission of these images into an easily assimilated vocabulary. Whatever difficulties we may encounter will only be illusions created by our own spiritual rigidities anyway...and the magic is in moving beyond these self imposed limitations, which is **a physical as well as an emotional event**, that starts with the recognition that we are not separate. Any movement we initiate must be with the certainty that bodyworker and client are an equal part of the blend, and the magic is found in the compound...in moving past the illusions of our individual egos.

The magic comes on the truth of time which is the simple recognition of divinity. It's all out there for us, you know, and it's obscured only by that which, after all, is anchored in the physical tissues of the body.

To claim it is only a matter of honoring the demands of the body (at this point they are no longer requests) that we put our petty fears aside, recognize who we are, and place all of our energies into the equation.

The consequences are immediate and practical. From this perspective nothing can be effectively excluded from the equation. The linear dictum to get your underlying physics straight before you even consider metaphysics is an incomplete statement that does not apply in this multidimensional reality in which we find ourselves. The point that can no longer be ignored is that your metaphysics do more than just influence your physics. They are your physics!

***

"The most beautiful and most profound emotion one can experience is the source of the mystical. It is the source of all true science."

Albert Einstein

"I want to know God's thoughts...the rest are details"

Choosing Your Bodyworker

On with the game, and since it's played in pairs, find yourself a suitable partner. Just remember that it's a healing partnership we are talking about, not musical chairs! There is no shortage here so don't fall apart when the music stops. Grant yourself the luxury of a leisurely look around.

And while shopping remember that you are looking for a mirror and a metaphor. Choose your mirrors well and your metaphors cautiously.

Do you feel comfortable and secure in the presence of this person? Comfortable enough to sanction his or her joining you in the tracking down of your soul?

We are talking now about reaching the upper limits, but the bottom line is that bodywork from any professional will almost undoubtedly be of benefit. Bodywork of any variety is better than no bodywork at all...usually.

This is about discernment, about fine tuning, and about finding the most suitable partner of them all.

Trust your instincts. This selection procedure is really the beginning of your bodywork for **your instincts are rooted in your body,** and with this process you begin renewing an old and somewhat misunderstood relationship. Monitor your tissues every step of the way.

The choosing of your bodyworker is a two way process, a process of matching souls. Your body and your soul will work together on this. Bodies know very quickly about other bodies. They have their own language and speak very clearly to each other.

They have an instant understanding. It's our know-it-all minds that have been conditioned not to trust whatever they can't explain, so the rational mind pretends to ignore and then overrules the instincts of the body.

To align the instincts with the rational, there are certain traits we can consider on the conscious level. Of course no single profile can define such a diverse group as bodyworkers.

However, the most successful bodyworkers do tend to have certain characteristics in common. There are certain factors that seem to predict success more often than not. Indicators which might also answer the question of why bodywork is sometimes an outstanding process of personal growth, while at others only a relaxing back massage, equally rewarding but on different wavelengths. These factors may even discriminate between the artists and the technicians.

If there is any one element that runs throughout all good bodywork, then **it will be found within that special space where boundaries fade as bodyworker**

and client connect without illusion.

The healing element may certainly be found within the bodyworker's technique, and absolutely within his application, but even more so within this relationship that transcends both the mechanics and the philosophy.

I noticed that those clients getting the best results often used the same words: "I trust you totally." But what does that mean? Trust me to do what? I hadn't done anything particularly trustworthy. Their words didn't seem to fit our transactions. But when they said this magical phrase good things began to happen.

I meditated on it and came to understand that they were talking of a different kind of trust. They were talking in the organic sense, of trust on a cellular level. The tissues themselves were confident that I would respect their integrity, and honor their little whimsicalities. They knew I would not place my priorities over theirs. And with this acknowledgement our relationships moved into new stages, where the tissues increasingly honored me with their most serious of secrets.

As their confidence in my integrity grew, as they became absolutely certain that I wouldn't abuse their trust, even unwittingly, they often gave me the grand tour of the soul. They understood that I had surrendered to them, and then they too felt safe enough to surrender to the Universe.

This phenomenon of surrender has an interesting nature about it. Its parameters are so elusive that, to totally understand it, one must experience it.

Body Secrets

Trust is a major aspect, but it's only one aspect. Surrender has all the appearances of honor and respect and acceptance, but it is also much more than that. It's more than an inner knowledge of safety, more than the sum of all its qualities. It's a state of love, a total and unconditional acknowledgement, a dismantling of all defensive structures, a condition of the heart as much as the soul. There are only winners in this type of surrender. All you ever give up are your limitations.

So how does one find a bodyworker with these qualities? Someone likely to gain the complete trust of your tissues, someone they can resonate with?

The first place to look is to his or her structure, particularly to his rigidities. When he moves does all of him move at the same time? Do his movements travel throughout his body? Is there a sense of Harmony within his body?

Movement patterns can define your worker for you quite accurately. Is this the metaphor you choose to follow?

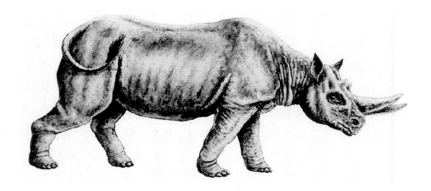

190

Choosing Your Bodyworker

Does he embody the work that he does? If he works within a system, does his body represent all the best qualities of that system? Most schools require a certain amount of their bodywork as a prerequisite for training. This lets their principles soak into the tissues. Does this bodyworker wear his principles easily and are they the principles you are looking for?

Does he breathe? He may be alive, but that doesn't mean he breathes! Does he really breathe? Which may possibly be the most important trait of all.

At the heart of good bodywork is a full and conscious breathing, not only by the client but equally so by the bodyworker. This is not the minimal amount of oxygen necessary to sustain life, I mean **a breath!** ...a continuous pattern of full and effective oxygen exchange throughout the body.

My experience is that the most efficient form of breathing is the natural form, the more natural the better, breathing such as the conscious breathing that's being practiced in major rebirthing circles. It's certainly not the only effective method available, it's just the most consistently beneficial, by a long shot, that I've so far been able to find.

It's difficult to consider breathing and bodywork and not consider rebirthing at the same time. Bodywork and rebirthing go hand in hand, two sides of the same coin. When the community of rebirthers merge their talents with the community of bodyworkers, everyone benefits, the bodyworker, the rebirther, and their expanding circle of clients.

A rebirther needs ongoing bodywork to continually refine and keep his own skills up to date. It's even more essential that the bodyworker receive ongoing re-birthing. Both the bodyworker and rebirther are their own tools. There is a direct link between how well the bodyworker breathes and the quality of his work. Breathing alone is no guarantee of good bodywork but, on the other hand, it's difficult to the edge of impossible to find really good bodywork in the absence of breath. Breathing limitations in the bodyworker tend to perpetuate themselves in the client.

For greatest benefit, rebirthing should accompany your bodywork. It's something to do along with, rather than later, or instead of. Your bodyworker should be able to recommend a good rebirther to you.

How important do I consider it that my clientele rebirth? I have a substantial bias for breathers that reflects in my scheduling. It's more fun, as well as more professionally rewarding, to work with them. I notice that the quality of my work improves in direct ratio to the quality of my client's breathing patterns. You would do well to make effective breathing a priority in choosing your bodyworker.

There is nothing about us that's outside of the equation. Our bodies reflect it all back at our client. Every emotion, every tension, no matter how transitory, affects our work.

While we can usually recognize our moods and do something about them, it's our deeper and unsuspected patterns that limit us the most. It's these very patterns, so basic to all of our attitudes, that most undermine our results. To insure that we do our very best work, and to reach our highest capabilities, we need continual rebirthing, in exactly the same manner that we need continual body-work.

Look for a bodyworker who continually upgrades his skills. One who is not closed to any of the more esoteric dances of the universe. If he doesn't keep up his learning his growth stops, and his movement stops, and rigidities set in, and he becomes a little less alert to the constantly changing algebra of your body.

Consider the state of his Ego, which can form a colossal blockade to the free flow of information that is so fundamental and necessary to effective bodywork. I have been privileged to work with many of the world's greatest bodyworkers and I notice they all share a certain quality. Despite an acknowledged expertise and a considerable body of knowledge, once they begin to work, what becomes uppermost in their minds is how incomplete their knowledge really is. A recognition that frees them to approach each individual client as an open system. They can work with his patterns as they actually are in this particular moment, rather than just imposing yet another preconceived pattern on top of the heap.

One of the very best bodyworkers used to describe her work as "mucking around," yet another as "fiddling around." These might seem strange descriptions but they came from the *very best* of bodyworkers.

It may not be what we would expect to hear, or like to hear, but both of them were telling the absolute truth. They approached each new body wondering what they might find there. When the work started they had no room for their egos. Their lesson to each of us is not to look to our ego for security. Find it instead in your body and in your soul.

To be a bodyworker is to live in the inconsistent state of perpetual learning. Ida Rolf stressed the need for the rolfer to find his security within his constantly shifting framework of insecurity.

If your bodyworker comes from a point of certainty he is himself holding on to trembling shadows and his work will probably not reflect *your* highest possibilities.

Blame it on the ego. I hear bodyworkers, usually the very new ones, proclaiming: "I'm Good!" And it may be true. They may be very efficient with their technique, efficient at applying their moves very smoothly. Their clients may look better than when they started, and yes, they have done some good work. But without their attitudinal limitations could they have done even better? I think so. In fact, I have never failed to find it any other way!

Maybe their statement of proficiency is not a statement after all. It could be a prayer, or possibly an affirmation chanted as a balm to soothe their own insecurities.

But the play is the thing, and **you** are the star.

The bodyworker is a supporting actor. His purpose is to strengthen your performance. If you choose a bodyworker that is so completely full of himself, there may be no room in the process for you.

Body Secrets

To get the most from your work, choose a partner most likely to remind you of your own hidden magnificence.

Choose one who can help you unlock your own healer from within. One who can help you do it for yourself rather than try to do it for you. Look for the attitude of "I can help you get it" rather than "I can give it to you," an attitude that shares the responsibilities as well as the credits. Recognize that as client you do the actual healing on yourself anyway.

Match belief systems with your partner as your mirror. Be sure that the two of you at least allow for the same range of possibilities. It is from out of these belief systems that your results are shaped.

The loudspeaker at the Gym had a request for "someone to share a game of racketball." Such an appropriate and absolutely wonderful phrase: "share a game." For surely on some level the game was already in progress and this unknown voice just wanted a partner to step on the carrousel with him.

This is how it is with bodywork. Your game has already begun. Now you need to find yourself a partner to share the game with. The key word is **share**. What the two of you need between you is an equality, and an acceptance...not a competition.

This is important! Let your body search out and listen for the slightest trace of the competition mentality, then quickly sidestep it.

Look also for **courage.** In this archeological excavation of the body many suppressed experiences will be uncovered, which may be unsettling or even frightening to the uninitiated, but which must never be allowed to frighten your bodyworker. Which all too often it does unfortunately. Sometimes even to the point where the session is concluded prematurely, before your body has had time to assimilate its encounter with the face of an old fear.

Attention all Bodyworkers!

When the client unwraps an event, **you are obliged** to accompany that event to its resolution. You took an oath of office. It's in your contract. Her body has trusted you enough to risk this much exposure, and now you must validate that trust.

Clients who have been deserted in the middle of their unravelling always recognize that fact on some level, they seem to somehow understand that they have been abandoned.

I've come to spot most of these abandoned ones as soon as they enter my office. They appear incomplete and agitated, with a diffuse emotional vulnerability that sometimes borders on the suicidal.

Our job then is to pick up the threads where they have been dropped, to assist the pattern to complete its interrupted journey to release, and allow the entire body to exhale...at last. It is absolutely essential that we have the integrity to finish our task once we begin it.

The tissues must have complete confidence in us and know that we will take the trip with them all the way home and back again.

Body Secrets

I was once in a class where a bodywork technique of awesome potential was being presented. I witnessed an undercurrent of rebellion directed against the very effectiveness of the technique. Some of my classmates were openly afraid to incorporate it into their practice, while others struggled quite uncharacteristically to grasp the elements of its principles and applications.

Those who immediately took to the process had one obvious quality in common...a substantial amount of **pure joy.**

They enjoyed their life, they enjoyed the class, they enjoyed the unlimited potential of their work. I've since noticed that the most effective bodyworkers all seem to share this same sense of joy, and that it communicates to their clients on a tissue-to-tissue level.

Remember that **your tissues like to laugh**. Look for the laughter in your bodywork partner. Look for one who can stir up the revelry lying dormant within your cells. One who can invite it out to play, who can enlighten and enliven your body and help your tissues dance.

But your body already knows all this. This is only a guideline for the rational mind.

The caveat to all this, is that the very best may look nothing at all like we think a bodyworker should. They might not match our pictures in the least. So look at their results. Listen to their words....but listen most attentively to your own body....and let it override all your other considerations. These guidelines are only for when your head is a little congested.

"What If....."

Questions I Have Known and Loved.

Certain concerns always seem to surface in one guise or another. When passed through a sieve the following common threads emerge.

The Length of a Session. Almost always the number one concern of bodyworkers anywhere in the world. I never fail to hear it and like most good questions the answer is just logical enough to be overlooked. Just as Abraham Lincoln said the legs need to be long enough to reach the ground, a session needs to last until it's over. Your session is finished when your work is done.

Although accurate this answer is highly unsatisfactory to those who don't speak Body as yet. When you learn Body, when you can consult and trust what the body tells you, the question will never again be asked.

The problem is created by the common practice of referring to sessions as *hours*. An *hour* originally referred more to the sequence of a formula than to the length of time spent with the client. We have become prisoners of our own sloppy semantics. We book our clients by the hour, we expect to work an hour, and our clients expect to be worked on for an hour.

Yet the length of the session has little to do with its quality. There are many of us who feel guilty if we end a session in less than an hour. We stall to eat up the clock and finish out the time. It's an attitude that depreciates our work and tends to dissociate us from that class of professionals where we belong.

Value and time do not equate. I was once heavily into Esalen massage, where we spent a frustrating amount of time and energy trying to compact the work into a three hour package without sacrificing quality.

I have also worked in the framework of a full six-hour-per-day weekend, practicing a form of very old Mongolian massage. It was, in effect, one long continual session administered over two full days.

At the other end of the scale I have worked within a fairly strict framework of fifteen minute Chiropractic treatments.

Each of these formats produces stories of great therapeutic success. Value received is completely outside of any time frame. The essential factor is that the *tissues not be rushed.* So allow for a longer introductory session in order to become acquainted with all the little idiosyncrasies of these tissues.

My initial sessions usually span from forty-five minutes to an hour and a half. Thereafter the length of time varies considerably. I process some clients in half an hour, others require forty-five minutes, and others an hour. A few require even longer attention, but the answer is always the same: *learn the body parameters of the individual*...and then follow them.

Fees. Sooner or later everyone gets around to this. But it's really an extension of the first question. If you want to charge for your time by the hour, then do so. Just beware the trap of clock watching. My preference is to charge by the session.

The cost of a session varies from nation to nation as well as regionally within a country. We have a product of great value that is undersold more often than not. Wherever the work gains status the fees increase. Results tend to be rewarded. A successful practitioner can command respect as a professional therapist and should be paid accordingly, at whatever the going rate happens to be for that area.

Toxins, Negativity, & Burnout. A common area of questioning concerns protecting ourselves from the negativity of certain clients, avoiding released toxins, and burn out. Which is your basic three part question, in which each part is an element of the same process.

The first is not much of a problem if you select your clients with care. There are some people out there who are toxic to you, whose presence can drain you to the point of exhaustion in just a few moments. Learn to recognize these people. Listen to your body, it won't lie to you. Stay away from these people.

Never, never, never take one on as a client...unless of course you choose to.

But choose consciously. They can deplete your energy, and leave you in a state where your physiological defenses are weak and ineffectual, and then you are open to every type of infection currently making the rounds, and some original ones besides.

Work with a genial clientele and there is no negativity directed at you, so there is none to defend yourself against. However, the work does release toxins that can be depleting to your resources. The effects of these toxins range all the way from an unpleasant odor, to a debilitating tiredness, to an illness that can cut short your practice.

For protection look first to the physical setting of your workplace. Abundant sunlight along with fresh air and plant life are musts. Candles and incense both protect and purify the environment, as does a negative ion generator.

To cleanse your space, place a half-inch or so of Epsom salts in a saucepan, barely cover it with rubbing alcohol, and then light it. Carefully. It makes a big flame. Carry this torch throughout your office, lingering around the immediate areas of toxic concentration.

Sage and other selected herbs may also be burnt. There is an endless variety of individual power objects that can keep your space clear. Examples are crystals or other gem stones, power roots, any power-programmed event. A shrine, pictures of saints, holy men, teachers, or gurus can also purify the atmosphere.

Water washes away most everything. Scrub well following each session, being careful to first rinse thoroughly with *cold* water, before using soap and hot water.

Toxins also attach themselves to fabrics. A change of clothes is like a fresh beginning. Experiment with frequent changes and feel how invigorating it can be for your body.

Note how it affects your work.

Chanting affirmations will program your tissues. Many bodyworkers start their work day as well as each individual session with some variation of the mantra: "I will not accept anything into my body that I would not consciously choose to invite in."

Quite possibly the single most widely used method of defense is the calling down of the white light and working under its protection.

This is an all purpose umbrella covering every situation of concern.

The state of your body itself may be your best defense. Center your structure and your energy. Work in a state of balance that offers no restriction to the natural flow of rhythm throughout your body. Toxins have difficulties with such a body for there is little foothold to which they can cling.

As to **burn out,** again be selective about your clientele. Note how your body reacts in the presence of prospective clients. Do they nourish you? Do their interests in this association match your own? Would you choose to spend time with them without the money factor? Listen to your body and trust it. It knows what it talks about.

You may choose to refer a client to another bodyworker. This is a legitimate decision, not a cop out at all. Working with a mismatch can be a wearing experience. It's not only the two of you who suffer, it's all your other clients as well. And down goes your productivity.

You are much more effective when you follow your preferences and work with those you take real pleasure in. Your enjoyment reflects in the quality of your work and strongly influences the answer to the following question.

How Many Sessions can you do in a day or a week? As you can see, this addresses the concepts of abundance and scarcity. The answer is dependent on the resolution of the previous question, and ultimately upon your own self imposed limitations.

Once upon a time I was heavily into struggle and scarcity, which seem to go together, and I worked very hard. Some days I did as many as six sessions and I always worked a full five day week. I earned a reputation as a hard worker and by God I deserved it! Then by chance, within a period of one week, I met two quite efficient bodyworkers and each did ten sessions a day on a regular basis. This possibility was new to me, and it liberated me. I actually had not realized that this was a viable option.

I had swallowed the myth of the day that one could work themselves into a state of exhaustion through an excess of sessions. In my area of the country agreement on optimal limits was four to six sessions a day, four days a week. Anything above this was severely pushing your luck.

But neither of these two radiated anything less than the highest quality of vigorous health. And their work itself was of superior quality.

The number of my own sessions increased immediately just as did the quality. I no longer worked hard. Just more efficiently.

I travel extensively now and my schedule is always busiest just before I leave. My clients often stage a last minute rush to get work that can no longer be put off. During these times I frequently work in excess of sixteen hours per day and it does not tire me at all.

Bodywork was not meant to be debilitating. When not on the road, I often choose to work a seven day week with six to twelve sessions per day. Part of the secret is that I love what I do. The other part is that my clientele is a continuing source of nourishment for me. My work helps keep me healthy. It's a matter of choice and abundance.

Standards of Evaluation: posture vs. function.

There are bodyworkers whose work originates from a concept of an ideal static posture just as there are those who emphasize function rather than form. Together they create an ideological battleground of structural symmetry vs. efficient movement.

This is an artificial and limiting conflict. They are only two aspects of the same reality anyway. We could label it dynamic vs. static posture as easily as structure vs. function. Any choice we make here is living in scarcity.

Their arguments are not real!
Symmetry does **not** have to equate with rigidity. This only follows when symmetry is **forced** onto a body.

Granted, the body is not constructed to be absolutely symmetrical. But on the other hand, the further the body wanders from a postulated symmetry, the more likely there is to be a problem, and the greater the effort needed for the body just to support itself. It's a matter of gravity and stress. Where the structure intersects with gravity in an inappropriate manner there will be stress. And tissue breakdown never lags far behind.

The more symmetrical, the more balance there is within a body, the more pleasing it is to the eye. And if the strict truth will be told attractive bodies are healthy bodies.

The more symmetrical the body the more graceful its movements. The body may move in asymmetry but there is a symmetricality about this asymmetry also. Movement and rigidity are the ones who don't get along together. It's important if only for health considerations to have free movement throughout the structure, no matter what the appearance of the structure. Free movement must never be sacrificed to any standard. **In honoring individual deviations from symmetry we thereby increase the possibility for further symmetry.** The secret is to encourage individual variations to the point of maximum ease, but never to the point of structural distortion.

Is pain a necessary part of bodywork? I don't think so. I see pain as serving no positive function at all. This is my understanding today. Years ago I reluctantly endorsed all the common myths of the day concerning pain and bodywork. I relied on them for reassurance since I knew that my bodywork hurt. It didn't help that clients described it as a good hurt, somehow even that didn't sound quite right. Pain hurts. So I blamed it on my clients.

In my own role of client I had accepted the rhetoric that because of my resistance to change, I created my own pain. But I also experienced the contradiction of my greatest gains being associated with my most painless sessions.

The complicating factor is that the face of pain does have this other side to it: The client's own *attitude*. Those with a true willingness to go for it no matter what will definitely experience less discomfort, no matter how harsh or intrusive the technique might be.

It is also said (with occasional truth) that it isn't really pain at all, just a misinterpreting of an extremely intense experience. But I knew I could tell the difference. Intense experiences felt good, pain hurt.

I also know the litany of the Gym. No pain, no gain. Everything worthwhile has a price tag attached to it. You've got to pay the price.

But this is bodywork. This is spiritual growth. We are moving into the light here. That misunderstood chant of the Gym doesn't apply.

My present understanding of pain is that it is *totally counterproductive*. The only time I give pain now is when I don't know enough **not** to give pain, or when I neglect to listen to the body before me. I consider pain to be my fault completely, never my client's.

Even if my client is resistive to change, if I can listen closely enough to his body I can slip past the resistances.

But the myth dies hard. A few clients are still heavily committed to struggle. They expect and welcome the pain. Pain they understand. They know how to overcome obstacles. What bewilders them are the profound results associated with such a light and pleasurable touch.

It's part of the if-it-tastes-bad-it-must-be-good-for-you mentality. How is it possible for both growth and enjoyment to be in the same package? How can it feel good and be good for you at the same time? We all know that's ridiculous. Change always hurts! (According to a required text in Psychology I once studied...on the Graduate level no less.)

It's the old and honorable battle between what is seen and felt and experienced, standing in direct opposition to the conditioned wisdom of the intellect.

Which leads us to the question of just **who this work is appropriate for.**

It's appropriate for whomsoever has an interest in it. That's who! (Thank you, Judith.)

Does the work last? About midway into his first session this becomes the number one concern of the new client. It's another aspect of the struggle-and-overcome theme once again. If they are getting such good results so easily, how can they possibly hold up?

One way to envision our work is to see ourselves removing pins from the fabric of the tissue. **Pins** in a very literal sense. Pins of compression and adhesion. Once we remove them the tissue will not easily nor voluntarily allow itself to be repinned. When we erase the physical residue of a traumatic experience the body remembers that it once held title to this area and reaffirms its functional ownership once again. It feels more comfortable with the pins removed. The ego may try to sidestep this unfamiliar state of ease, but the body won't have any part of it. It happily accepts this comfortable state of affairs.

Every characteristic of the body exists within a pattern, within a pattern that is itself a variable in the equation, a pattern caught in the endless ebb and flow of creation and re-creation. The pins rely on this process for their very existence. But we can alter the process itself.

The ego thinks the name of the process is Eternal. Then we remind the body that it is only a process, and that its real name is Change. As we work with any structural situation we are also working with its processes, its patterns. It's just as easy to concentrate on the process as it is on the form. The secret is that the process and the form are actually one and the same thing.

The old pattern is gone.

The king is dead. Long live the king!

Does the work last? Not in the form it's in now it doesn't. The change doesn't last, it continues changing, and growing, and its influence resounds throughout the system. Does the work last? No! It just gets better and better.

Is total recovery possible following soft tissue or even joint injury?

Conventional wisdom dictates that, following an injury, a part can never again be as good as it once was. My mind understood the rationale behind this dictate and accepted it as truth. Then my experience began to make a liar of my mind. Over and over I witnessed countless contradictions, but still I looked outside my experience for confirmation. An experienced and respected colleague illuminated my personal limitations for me. She allowed that it was not only possible to be as well as before, it was possible to become even better. Which was only telling the truth as she had observed it.

I had witnessed the same outcome myself countless times, but I always failed to consciously acknowledge the situation. I saw and I knew, and now I even acknowledge that given the exposure of a body to a more harmonious relationship between its parts, it often elects to function smoother than it ever has previously.

As stress goes out, grace-through-movement comes in, and the body feels good. Health and movement have this thing together. We see a sensual grace rhythmically undulating throughout the soft tissues and around and about and within the structure of the joints themselves. Rhythms of necessity. Rhythms to lubricate. The choice is to lubricate or degenerate. Movement exercise reminds the joint to renew itself. We can help it exercise either actively or passively, my preference is both.

Speaking of exercise, I've heard that it's unwise to exercise during your bodywork processing. This is another myth. Not only is it appropriate to exercise, it actually enhances your processing.

It is also never a question of which exercise you do, but how you do whatever exercise you choose to do. Its never what you do, it's always how you do it.

Is jogging good for you? Depends on how you jog. To answer I would have to watch your jogging habits. The practice in sports medicine is to speak in terms of efficiency and stability rather than good or bad. This shifts the emphasis to where it more properly belongs. The important point is the state of your biomechanics within the event, not the event itself.

Another myth is that you should only have one type of bodywork processing at a time, that the benefits of one brand of bodywork will interfere with those of another. This is seldom the case. Good work multiplies rather than subtracts. We are each too big to be encompassed by only one system. Every good process will benefit us, even more so when they are applied at the same time. Each enhances the other. Rebirthing is an example of a process that will magnify benefits from any brand of bodywork.

How is Body Harmony different from any other processing?

It isn't. But then again maybe it is. It originates out of abundance, and cooperation, and networking. It goes beyond the limits of standard bodywork in that its structure and its format and its design always shift to meet those of the client. It's a completely open system with constantly expanding parameters. We try to avoid totally the myth of separation. Nothing that works is ever excluded.

Practitioners themselves are central to the equation. Body Harmony can not be practiced from a purely objective stance. To swim you must first be in the water.

We are a band of equals. Our lack of hierarchy invites a wide range of input and promotes constant creativity. The work itself lives in a ongoing state of growth and synthesis. It can successfully be incorporated into any established bodywork practice no matter what form that practice may take. It never erases, it only supplements.

If I can't quite speak the language as yet, and I don't have a map, **where do I begin?**

Depends on the client! The breath is always a productive place to start. It influences everything everywhere. As we affect the breathing pattern we affect the entire biochemistry of the body.

The work itself becomes diagnostic. Whatever you do points the way to what comes next. Follow the trail of the breath throughout the body and notice what areas cry out for more. Answer their call and watch for even further changes that escort your touch. With every touch and every release your formula changes, a previously well hidden area of tension is uncovered and **before you know it you are speaking Body.**

Scars are exceptionally worthy of our attention. Old scars especially are masters of the subtle sabotage. They speak with a voice that is heard and respected throughout the body. As you address a scar all its support systems listen to your words and bring themselves to your attention. The consequences of working on scars are both far reaching and diverse. It touches on long term problem areas and encourages them to mediate their grievances. When the scar surrenders, situations that have traditionally resisted all solution surrender along with it. All this scar really wanted was to be treated with a little respect.

Can you teach an old scar new tricks?

Oh yes. With gentle attention, the quality of scar tissue itself will soften and blend with the surrounding tissue. I have worked on the neonates, on scars scarcely a day old and found that such quick attention following an injury or an operation is incredibly helpful to a speedy and complete recovery process.

I've also worked on the old timers. Very old timers. One such inch-deep adhesion had camped in the abdominal musculature for over half a century. A full one inch depression and I watched it fade out and all but disappear almost immediately. A fifty year old scar that, just like everything else about the body, proved to be more of a process than a thing. **Just because it has always been there, doesn't mean that it always has to be there.**

Complying with a common misunderstanding that they could injure themselves, a great many clients, possibly the majority, have avoided touching their scar areas altogether.

Those who have since been taught how to physically work with their scars report a vast difference in the tissue itself as well as a continual improvement in their overall health.

What if I don't want to deal with the psychic aspects of this work? You may choose not to be involved in these matters, but the truth is that it's already **too late!** If you are involved with the body at all, then you are already dealing with its psychic aspects. It's impossible to work in any depth without engaging the psychic, which is only an extension of the flesh. As you free the tissue from its stockades of compression you also uncage all the memories locked within.

Is it so surprising then that some of these memories touch on lives lived before this one? This only means that a certain *tendency* came in with the client. Recalling the incidents behind it and releasing them can clear the results of several lifetimes in one stroke.

There is also another psychic event that many experienced body workers meet at one time or another, usually reluctantly. My first encounter was certainly not of my choosing.

I am speaking of **possession and exorcism.** If you work on bodies long enough, and you speak their language well enough to touch their core, you will probably become involved with an exorcism. I have never started a session with this intention, but they have frequently come up and introduced themselves.

My first experience was my most fearsome experience. As unsettling as the encounter was, I quickly found that either I could not, or would not, back off. (I'm still not sure which it was.) I had no choice but to accept the experience for what it was. So I called down the white light and bathed myself in its protection. I kept my body as balanced and graceful and as loose as I could, and I prayed quite a bit more than I had in a long time.

My hands reminded the tissues of how they once had been, and the entity released its hold and departed. Not as dramatically as I would have imagined, but depart it did. The energy shifted and the perspiration evaporated. The client was exhausted but peaceful. Her rigidities were no more...her pain had resolved and her tissues relaxed...and stayed relaxed.

Looking back now I understand that what I did was neither courageous nor unusual. I was only doing my job as a bodyworker. Simply and naturally helping the body to rid itself of yet another barrier. It's no more than Ida Rolf would have expected of us.

How much of this work is mind over matter? None! This concept simply does not work. It is never mind over matter, it's always mind and matter, **mind in conjunction with matter.**

You can join nature, but you can't beat her. It is never a question of overcoming, it's a surrendering and becoming one with.

Your passport is the certainty that your thoughts have an influence on your results. Thoughts are creative. Your attitudes and your visualizations can and do shape your world. This is not just the traditional positive thinking here. There is no denial of the way things happen to be at this juncture, this is just the recognition that we are responsible for our own experience and can shape it from here on in.

I celebrated a recent New Year's Eve by participating

in the physical affirmation of a thirty-five foot fire walk. It was my first fire walk but the principles were completely clear after only a few moments. Any martial artist knows them, as does the dancer, or any dedicated athlete in any sport. It's a matter of intention, keeping yourself congruent and focusing on your goal.

Moments before the walk began a key question was raised. Who among us would be willing to accept a few small blisters in order to achieve their goal?

Some of my mates accepted this as a reasonable price to pay for a victorious encounter. My body was adamant. It rejected the suggestion out of hand. Blisters would be no victory at all. Why should I accept such limits on my experience? I wasn't out to conquer or overcome anything (except my own limitations), if the fire were truly my friend, as I suspected, then it wouldn't burn me. Along with the majority of those present I elected not to accept any blisters whatsoever, no matter how insignificant they might be.

A few of the participants jumped off the coals without finishing, some skipped the walking altogether, others completed the walk and collected their blisters. I talked with a few of the latter and sure enough, they had accepted their blisters beforehand. The majority of us didn't even have a red mark as a reminder.

To my body the walk felt exactly like thirty-five feet of cool grass. Quite a few others experienced the sensation of warm sand. One middle aged lady reported it felt exactly like walking on marshmallows.

To some the event seemed too easy, too simple somehow. Almost immediately people began denying their experience. They had followed the instructions as given. They had experienced the creative power of their thoughts. But they expected a struggle and they didn't get it. They discovered instead that there really was nothing to struggle with, there was nothing to overcome, and for some this was the most difficult concept of all to incorporate into their lives.

The whole point of the walk was that it was not a mystical experience outside of your everyday existence, it was a central part of that existence brought into consciousness. I have certainty that I didn't conquer the fire. The fire was my brother.

I also know that I was not alone on the walk. Jesus was there, so how could I possibly be hurt? I was at one with nature, not in opposition to her. Mind and matter were singing a duet.

What are the limitations of bodywork?

What can bodywork not do? I don't know what it can not do. The limitations of bodywork are not found somewhere out there. Its limitations are our limitations and are found in our own thoughts and in our own bodies. When considering limitations, remember that thought is creative, and remember that the principle works in both directions, it can just as easily expand your potential as compress it.

I hesitate to place limitations on bodywork. They would only be **my** limitations and not apply necessarily to anyone else. They would be a disservice to everyone involved. An acknowledged limitation becomes a judgement and a sentence. My preference is to work without any such handicap.

I once worked on a fellow bodyworker from Atlanta, Georgia. Together we discovered an internal scarring of considerable proportions within her left elbow. At least a quarter-inch in cubic bulk. A situation that, at the very least, takes months to work out. I was sure about this timetable of recovery, or at least I thought I was sure of it. I also knew that it might not be my knowledge but my limitation. So the two of us worked together outside of time.

She had me put her in touch with the exact physical definitions of the scarring. As I contacted the scar tissue she did the same. Together we explored the parameters of holding. In less than five minutes she succeeded in completely dissolving her fibrosis.

Mind over matter? Not at all. She just spoke fluent Body, knew that thought was creative, and didn't place artificial limitations on herself.

Are there ways to learn bodywork outside of the school framework?

Yes there are. Just take your hand, and with intention and awareness place it upon the body of another...and you can do it now.

"Whatever you can do, or dream you can, begin it. Boldness has genius, power, and magic in it."

Goethe

Which is just one of the ways to remind yourself that you already know the process. However, I do urge you to attend every school and every seminar you possibly can. Any massage school can give you some basics to get you started. Then take as many different classes, and as many different treatments as you can, in order to broaden your scope of knowledge.

Practice whatever you learn. Practice without the limitations you may have been taught. Let every client become your own unique and private seminar in bodywork. Work with an unremitting awareness, attending to the very smallest whisper from the body. The rewards are double, for **when you touch another with such awareness you open up for observation that same area within yourself.** You will be brought to an awareness of your own inner spaces. An awareness that is in itself an effective way to learn about bodywork.

Become your own laboratory. Receive bodywork of every type. Embody the principles into your structure. Incorporate them into your body and into your work and into your life. Network as you learn. Exchange bodywork with other bodyworkers and solicit their feedback.

Adopt an effective framework of success. You might contact the Loving Relationships Training seminars and look into their principles. Working within that context you may find that any limitations you place on yourself or your practice are only so much smoke.

Listen to your clients. Learning Body language is just like learning any other language. Fluency develops with practice and attention to detail.

So find yourself an enlightened client who will tell you what to do.....

.....and then do it!

"In other words...."

....to be a bodyworker.........

"Treat people as if they are what they ought to be and help them to become what they are capable of being."

Goethe

Comments from some who play the game
.......and play it well

Following a few advanced seminars in Sweden I solicited tips from a number of bodyworkers whom I considered to be particularly adept. I asked each to write a brief synopsis of what they personally considered the most basic principles underlying their work.

They were a varied lot, with interests representing the entire spectrum of healing as well as all aspects of the human potential movement. Although English was a second language for most, my preference has been to let their syntax stand as delivered. Their words have an eloquence that comes from the heart.

Their principles lend themselves to no distinct categories, so my arrangement is somewhat capricious. The voice of each bodyworker is presented separately. It is interesting to note the differing emphasis that each gives to his work.

***

"The most important is not who is patient or doctor. You heal yourself through the way you treat others and vice versa.

Everything literally is changing all the time, you are, and the one you are working on is.

Stars, trees, birds, earth, people are changing every second.

When you are working, and are putting your hand on somebody, your hand is changing in its cells and the other's cells are changing."

***

"It's not you who moves the tissue. It is the tissue who moves you. Somebody understood what I was saying the tissue says."

***

"I don't heal, I help the patient's body to heal itself."

***

"Everything is flowing. It is not only the blood in the body which is flowing but also the whole body being in constant motion. If one as a human being is supposed to function with a body and a soul which are in harmony, none of the body's energy-flows should be blocked. With body-work one helps the body, in a soft and benevolent way, to release the tensions and barricades that stop or obstruct the energy-flows. Without administering any chemical substances to the body and with no other tools than the hands, one is able, in what can be seen as an almost miraculous way, to cure a body and a mind which have fallen out of balance; and pain that has been there for years maybe, without having been observed on X-rays nor in laboratories, disappears. If one bears in mind that the body is a flowing unit striving for balance these changes become easier to comprehend."

...and the following came from a bodywork tyro but a highly respected teacher in his own field, with an acknowledged expertise in biochemistry. He came to his first hands-on bodywork class already conversant with Body language. He immediately recognized the principles as the same ones he had functioned under and honored all his professional life, he just needed to incorporate the knowledge into his hands.

"The main principle that has developed for me is an expanded awareness and honoring of each person's structure. The awareness of my own body and what it is communicating, and the awareness of the patient's tissue has opened up for me new eyes and areas, new possibilities in more effectively helping others and myself.

I can only properly honor each person's structure and function if I am in communication with it, which starts with awareness. True change is precipitated by awareness. Each session should be foremost awareness, communicating with the body by slowly moving in, respectingly lovingly, listening to the tissue and then following [along] with it, let the person's structure speak and communicate, don't lead, follow when you do this tissue dance.

What I experienced will carry on into areas of my professional and personal life."

Opening the door........

"The bodies are one with nature and they feel best when they decide the speed themselves."

***

**"Don't push it. Don't force it.
Let it happen naturally.
It will surely happen if it was meant to be."**

***

"Let the energy flow and
 follow the stream,
sensitivity, openness and balance is the most important,
finish with a prayer of blessing."

and....

***

"Try to empty myself like a zero.
Put on my hands and try to speak to the personality and feel what is going on inside."

and keep.......

"In Other Words..."

"Breathing"

***

"A relaxed body and a loose jaw."

"Eyes open and open to reactions in other parts of the body."

so.....

"Trust your intuition."

***

"Have an idea about what you would like to have done, being flexible enough to change if the body is up to something else."

***

"Be ready to chase after the tissues.
Even if your mind tells you something else from the beginning."

***

"Never stop learning from the tissues.
 Be gentle and work with respect."

and be sure to...........

"Always balance out your work."

***

"Always balance and let body integrate."

"See that patient is not on a Merry Go Round."

"Work with your own hands as your tools and work with the body and soul as one unit. If you are working with a pattern coming out from what you learned from patients you treated before, you are working with those and not with the one you have in your hands."

***

"Never use one pattern on every person. Every person is unique, and work on that principle."

therefore......

"Allow yourself to feel, and follow patients' wishes and reflexes, in body and spirit.
Never force, demand, or provoke."

***

"Listen to the body as well as to the patient."

***

"Listen to the body, be patient."

***

"It's important as a therapist to be relaxed in the whole body."

***

"Work with a peaceful concentrated mind."

***

"Breathe."

and maintain:

an attitude of gratitude..........

"For me it is always being able to give bodywork with love and to like the body with which I am working. I become happy and grateful if I have been able to make an improvement on the person that I have been working with and if the patient has accepted what I have done."

an awareness of...........

"The principle of awareness, more directly awareness of one's body, is one of the most important, if not the most important details in order for change to occur. In order to experience change, one has to take the responsibility for understanding and being aware of the pain one has.

One also must be taught to take the responsibility in becoming aware of the degree of pain through movement, because movement is what we are going for. A non moving part is a non working part, which contributes to a non functioning body. Awareness makes change possible and as much as one wants one can have. Have faith and go with it."

and always keep learning........

"The most important for a body worker is love for the human. After that comes a sensitive feeling hands, then a good lesson in practice and I think that must go on forever. I will learn new things all life long. If I trust in a higher life, it's really good."

Body Secrets

and in the vernacular...........

"The body is the teacher which always knows what it needs."
***

"Let your hand understand the tissues. It makes a movement...make the exact movement, and duplicate it with the hand.

And the tissue says,..Oh, some people understand me, and it gets rid of the blockage."

***

"The tissue is contracted, you make the same movement which it is trying to say.

You contact it in the same direction and help it.

And it feels the contraction

And it releases

The hand says Yes, I duplicate what you said."

***

**"Be aware what you give the patient.
Give love."**
***

"To work with love and joy and take what the body gives you with nice and soft hands"

***

"To be able to ask the right questions"

***

"Always teach love to the body you treat."

"In Other Words..."

and............

"Give a small prayer every now and then."

and most importantly..........

"Listen to the body's song

........and join it!"

You are never alone.

Illustrations

The artwork that appears on pages 14,132,186, 190, 193, 195, was created specifically for this publication by Yoka Laba of New York City.

About the Author.......

Don McFarland has impressive credentials as both a healer and a teacher. He appears to collect healing techniques as others might collect stamps or rare coins. He pursues the traditional as well as the more esoteric healing techniques.

He is a licensed Doctor of Chiropractic with a specialty in Dancemedicine, which helps the artistic athlete achieve his full potential. He has studied sports medicine with Dr. Leroy Perry Jr. of the International Sports Medicine Institute.

At the same time he is a cranial sacral therapist who follows not only the Chiropractic and the Osteopathic understandings but various mystic models as well.

There is more, much more. He was trained and certified as a Rolfer by Dr. Ida Rolf.

He studied Rosen therapy with Marion Rosen of the Rosen Institute.

He was certified as an Aston-Patterning teacher by Judith Aston. The list goes on and on. It's forty plus and rising.

It includes seemingly countless forms of massage as well as physical, energy, and psychic healing methods.

He continually travels the world to experience and study the less traditional methods of healing.

Less traditional, he points out, only in the eyes of the Westerner. There is literally no place he will not go in pursuance of his craft. He seeks out the best of healers and shamans and bodyworkers of every persuasion.

He is an original orchestrator of the non-systemic system of Body Harmony and is responsible for its introduction into more than twenty countries.

All of which he labels "prologue."